McGraw-Hill Series in Health Education,
Physical Education, and Recreation
CLIFFORD LEE BROWNELL, *Consulting Editor*

Body Dynamics

*McGraw-Hill Series in Health Education,
Physical Education, and Recreation*

CLIFFORD LEE BROWNELL, *Consulting Editor*

Body Dynamics

ELEANOR METHENY, Ph.D.

PROFESSOR OF EDUCATION AND PHYSICAL EDUCATION

UNIVERSITY OF SOUTHERN CALIFORNIA

First Edition

McGraw-Hill Book Company, Inc.

NEW YORK   TORONTO   LONDON

1952

BODY DYNAMICS

Preface

HUMAN FITNESS and efficiency are not new subjects. They have been discussed frequently and in detail by physiologists, kinesiologists, and physical educators. Much has been written which is of value to those working professionally in the general area of exercise and body mechanics. Little has been written for the general reader.

This book is written for the general reader who is interested in improving his own physical efficiency. It deals with the problems of fitness in terms of the efficient expenditure of human energy to produce maximum results with minimum effort. Scientifically sound information about the functioning of the human body and how it may be improved is presented in simple, nontechnical language. Ways in which the physical condition of the body may be improved by appropriate exercise are described, and modern principles of posture, movement, and relaxation for efficiency in work and play are discussed. Individual differences in structure and function are recognized, and all techniques for evaluation of posture and movement are adapted to individual use.

The materials presented were developed during eight years of experimentation with high school, college, and adult groups interested in increasing their own fitness for daily living. The reactions of these groups provided the basis for many revisions of both the content and the manner of presentation. Each group contributed in some way to the confirmation of two beliefs: first, that the fundamental principles for efficient functioning of the human body can be taught simply to intelligent persons who have no scientific knowledge of anatomy and physiology, and second, that an understanding of these principles can motivate action which results in improved physical efficiency. This book attempts to implement those beliefs.

It is designed primarily for use as a textbook for college freshmen in general physical education classes, but it is also written for the general adult reader. Much of the material can be used effectively with high school students, and the procedure described for individual evaluation of posture has been used successfully with elementary school children. For professional students in physical education, the book provides a simple, functional synthesis of materials covered in greater detail in courses in anatomy, physiology, kinesiology, and therapeutics. It should be of value to beginning teachers of physical education by helping them bridge the gap which now frequently exists between their knowledge of the basic sciences and their ability to impart, apply, and interpret this information in teaching high school pupils the fundamentals of exercise and functional body mechanics. Graduate students and experienced teachers also may find this simple presentation of materials helpful in redefining their concepts of the uses of exercise and its application to the solution of problems of posture and movement.

A book which attempts to develop an experimental idea is never finished, for the idea continues to grow, expand, and mature. It begins as a hazy, nebulous groping, an attempt to define, a need for understanding. It grows through experience; and if it is sufficiently encouraged by faith, enthusiasm, and cooperation, it eventually passes through its more awkward adolescent stages and achieves recognizable form and definition. It must then be tested in a pragmatic world to determine whether or not it is sufficiently useful to warrant its existence as an idea, a technique, or a method of doing something that is worth doing.

The idea on which this book is based has passed through its initial stages of growth. It was born during a war which brought the questioning of many traditions, beliefs, and long-established practices. It has grown through eight years of experience with students and teachers of all ages; their enthusiasm and cooperation fostered its growth and development; the encouragement of colleagues kept it alive through the heavy pressures of the war and postwar years; and the faith of students and coworkers provided the impetus for expressing it in writing. It must now undergo the pragmatic test to determine the direction of its further growth.

For the privileges of experience, cooperation, enthusiasm, encouragement, and faith, I am indebted to many people: the hundreds of students who have participated in my Workshop in Body Dynamics during the past eight years; the hundreds of teachers who have listened to me talk, questioned my ideas, and forced me to clarify my thinking; C. H. McCloy and Arthur Steindler of the University of Iowa, Katherine Wells of Wellesley College, Lucille Grunewald, now retired from the University of California at Los Angeles, and Charles LeRoy Lowman of the Orthopedic Hospital of Los Angeles—all of whom have contributed much to my understanding of body mechanics; Minnie L. Lynn of the University of Pittsburgh, who cajoled me into finishing the book; and all my beloved colleagues in the Department of Physical Education of the University of Southern California, each of whom has contributed in his own way to the development and completion of this undertaking.

ELEANOR METHENY

LOS ANGELES, CALIF.
November, 1951

Contents

Part I

INTRODUCTION

CHAPTER

1

Preview

MANY CENTURIES ago Plato said: "The most beautiful motion is that which accomplishes the greatest result with the least amount of effort." This is the concept of graceful movement; it is also the concept of efficiency. This book was written to expand that idea, to develop the basic principles of motion which make grace and efficiency possible, and to provide specific applications which will enable the reader to exemplify that idea in action.

This is a book about exercise, posture, and the mechanics of moving the body. It is concerned with the body as a moving and functioning machine which creates its own energy and expends it in every action of living. The conservation and expenditure of that energy is literally of vital importance to the individual, for it determines his capacity for physical activity. This book aims at increasing the physical efficiency of those who read it and apply it to their own actions; but because grace and efficiency are synonymous, it is also concerned with problems of appearance and aesthetics.

Energy is expended by the body during every living moment. This expenditure may be wasted in awkward movement, resulting in useless fatigue; it may be economical and efficient, producing results commensurate with the energy used. It is stupid to expend effort which accomplishes nothing; the sensible person utilizes his energy to produce the maximum amount of useful work with the least amount of effort.

Efficiency does not imply a stern philosophy of hard work and self-denial; it is the pleasant philosophy of constructive living, of eliminating useless strain, of conserving energy when its expenditure accomplishes nothing, of expending that energy freely and effectively, because it is available for work, for play, recreation, and the greater enjoyment of living.

The goal of ease of motion cannot be attained by a casual reading of this book. Some basic information is provided with suggestions for applying that information. The values to be derived from such knowledge will come only with persistent practice and application of those ideas. That is the responsibility of the reader.

Posture problems and the strains resulting from them are an old story. When prehistoric man first rose from four legs and attempted to balance himself upon two, he created a series of problems—mechanical, anatomical, physiological, and aesthetic—which affected all phases of his existence. He attempted to solve those problems by a process of trial and error, and eventually he learned to move about in an approximately upright position. His solutions of the problems involved were not always exact, economical, or artistic. His shoulders slumped. His chest became sunken. His abdominal muscles became slack, and he experienced difficulty in digesting his food. His feet hurt, and his back ached. His head dropped forward and his buttocks protruded backward. He found the upright position fatiguing, and as he slumped in body he became irritable in mind. His sleep was restless, and he suffered from insomnia. He paid a heavy price for the privilege of walking on two legs. It was miraculous that he succeeded in balancing himself at all.

Modern man considers himself immeasurably superior to his early ancestors, but the descendants of prehistoric man are still plagued with the same old postural problems. As they sit at a desk, stand before a machine, sweep a floor, or hang from a dangling streetcar strap, the forward heads, drooping shoulders, sagging abdomens, and protruding buttocks are distressingly evident. Their weary faces show the discontentment and pain which come from tired feet, aching backs, constipation, dys-menorrhea, and chronic fatigue. They walk with dragging steps, wasting energy they can ill-afford to spare in awkward move-ment. They struggle through their working days, straining their backs with inefficient effort, using brute strength as a poor sub-stitute for skill. Their recreation is joyless as they drag their tired bodies around the golf course, tense, nervous, and trying to improve their game by sheer determination, coming home fatigued almost to the point of exhaustion to drop into a rest-less, troubled sleep. Their energy is spent, they have accom-plished little, because they have never learned or practiced easy and efficient movement.

The younger generation fares no better. Apparently sup-plied with boundless energy, they rush from one activity to another, prodigally spending their strength in awkwardness and compensating for it by sheer enthusiasm—then absenting themselves from school or their jobs because of poorly func-tioning bodies. They spend hours on the tennis court and in the swimming pool, but still they walk up to receive their high school diplomas with their heads drooping, their abdomens protruding, and their hips swinging awkwardly under their academic gowns. Their brains may be fairly bursting with knowledge, but they are not physically educated so long as they continue to waste their physical energy in awkward move-ment.

The physically educated person knows more than the rudi-ments of the skills of games, sports, aquatics and dance. The physically educated person knows (1) how to conserve energy by proper use of the body and its parts, and (2) how to expend energy intelligently and efficiently to accomplish a given pur-pose. "Form" in all sports activities is based on an understand-ing of these two fundamental principles. So is form, efficiency, grace, ease—call it what you will—in the activities of daily living. This is the basis of physical education for efficiency and enjoyment.

Conservation of energy is essential in the busy modern world with its insistent physical demands. To walk, to run, to stand, to sit, to push, to rise, to pull, to lift, to carry throughout each day requires a great amount of energy. If these basic movements are performed awkwardly, much energy is dissipated, and needless fatigue occurs. If they are performed economically and skillfully, energy is conserved which may be expended in other profitable or pleasant undertakings. These movements may be analyzed mechanically, the easiest way of doing them determined, and this easiest way can—with practice—be learned until the easy performance becomes habitual. But there are many other work and play situations which cannot always be anticipated in detail. To provide for these situations, the basic *principles* of how to use muscles, levers, and joints to accomplish maximum work with minimum expenditure of effort should be thoroughly understood so that they may be applied in any performance involving body movement and the expenditure of body energy. These principles are not complicated. Their application can be illustrated in the performance of many typical tasks, and—again, with practice—their application in all situations can become habitual. With the thorough mastery of the skills of doing work the easy way should come the ability to rest while working and to relax while not working. Both the *how* and the *why* of these techniques are presented in this book in the belief that the understanding and application of these principles will do much to reduce the fatigue of students today and of the adults of tomorrow.

The intelligent expenditure of energy to accomplish a given purpose is also important. The exercise which comes from sports, games, dancing, and recreational activities has many values—physiological, psychological, and social—but this book is not concerned with that particular phase of physical activity except indirectly. It is concerned rather with the specific use of exercise to produce certain specific physical results.

It is easy to say, "Exercise is good for you," but the statement is not necessarily true until each word has been carefully defined in relation to the particular "you" under discussion. There are many kinds of exercise, each producing a particular effect, which in relation to the needs of a given individual may be either good or bad. There are many kinds of individuals, and the needs of one may not exist for another. The girl who sits all day at a desk with round shoulders and a forward head does not need forward bending; she needs straightening and stretching. The girl who runs a drill press with her feet does not need more leg exercise; but she may well need abdominal exercise or compensatory exercises to relieve the strain on certain muscles of her feet. The mother of a three-year-old child does not need activity; she needs relaxation.

The physically educated person should know how to evaluate his own exercise needs when such needs occur; he should be able to select the kind of exercise which will best meet his individual needs at that time. The person who depends entirely upon laxatives to "cure" constipation, who suffers from insomnia induced by nervous tension, or who believes that the way to remove excess body weight is to perform a newspaper-recommended set of exercises for five minutes a day, is not well-educated, regardless of the degrees and honorary scholarship keys he may have acquired. The educated person should know when exercise is needed, what kind of exercise is needed, and what results may be expected from the kind of exercise taken. He should have a well-learned "vocabulary of exercises" from which he may intelligently select what is needed to produce a given result. He may need none of them today; he may never need the aid of specific exercises to maintain his body in a condition of fitness for the work he does; but if such needs occur he should be prepared for them. He should know the uses and limitations of exercises for reducing nervous and muscular tension, for inducing sleep, for relieving menstrual pain, for correcting faulty body alignment, for controlling weight, for increasing the tonus or the strength of specific muscle groups, for relaxing or strengthening tired feet, for providing general organic stimulation; and, when they are needed, he should use them. It is one purpose of this book to provide such information and to try to promote a sufficient understanding of the principles underlying the uses of exercise to enable the reader to make full use of such kinds of exercise as he may need at present or at any time in the future.

Perhaps it should be stated here that this book is written in simple, nontechnical language. It reviews in a very elementary fashion many facts about the human body with which its readers are probably wholly or partially familiar. This is not a reflection on the intelligence of the readers; it is simply a recognition of the fact that the details of scientific terminology are easily forgotten and sometimes confusing, while the simpler, more general, and underlying principles are easily remembered. It is an attempt to make the basic materials of anatomy, kinesiology, and physiology functional information for the general reader, to make these materials so simple and so practical that they become a part of the background of general information which every educated individual acquires, which colors his thinking and actions without conscious effort to recall the exact details. This oversimplification has been done to try to assemble in one small volume the minimum essentials of body mechanics necessary to the practical application of the principles of exercise and movement to every phase of the life of the individual.

PROJECTS FOR FURTHER STUDY

1. Stand before a full-length mirror. Study your appearance as critically as if you were a stranger looking at you. Is your posture

attractive? Would you like to alter it? Walk toward the mirror and then back and forth in front of it. If you were a stranger, how would you react to the impression you make as you move and walk? Would you like to change that impression? How?

2. Consciously study the appearance of the people you see in the next two days. In your own mind hold a secret contest for the best posture, the best walk, and the best general pattern of movement. Briefly describe the winners.

3. In the same manner, hold a secret contest for the poorest posture, the poorest walk, and the poorest general appearance. Briefly describe "The Person I Would Most Like to Make Over!"

4. Write your name ten times with your right hand. Write it again ten times with your left hand. Note as many differences as you can in the two performances. Which was the more fatiguing? What is skill and coordination? How are they acquired?

2

Basic Structures

To UNDERSTAND the principles of movements it is necessary first to understand the basic structure of the body which performs those movements.

The body is built on a framework made of a few large bones and many smaller bones. There are more than 200 bones in all, but it is not necessary to know the names or even the locations of all of them in order to understand how the body moves. A knowledge of the general groups of large bones will be sufficient for this purpose. This knowledge will be increased by identifying these bones by locating them on the body. Explore them with the fingers to feel their shape and the way they are joined together.

The head, which is itself a hollow bony structure, rests on the *spinal column*. The spinal column is not made of one long bone, but of many small bones, resting one on top of the other and fitted together in a highly intricate fashion. The lower end of the spinal column is joined to a broad triangular bone at the lower part of the back.

This triangular bone is attached to two V-shaped bones, one on either side, which meet in front of the body. This girdle of bone is called the *pelvic girdle*. There are hollows in this bony girdle on each side of the body, and into these hollows are fitted the tops of the long bones of the upper leg (Figure 1).

The bone of the upper leg in turn rests upon the two bones of the lower leg and is joined to them at the knee. The bones of the feet make approximately a right angle with the bones of the leg and are joined to them at the ankle.

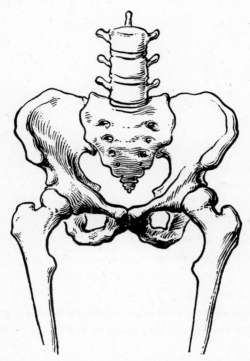

Fɪɢ. 1. The upper leg bones are attached to the pelvic girdle at the hip joints.

Returning to the upper part of the spinal column, attached to each of the small spinal bones (*vertebrae*) are two narrow flat bones which curve around the body and meet in front. These are the *ribs,* and they are joined in front to a flat bone extending vertically up the center of the chest (the *sternum*). The ribs form a hollow cage which encloses the heart and the lungs. Attached to the top of the rib cage in front are two long narrow bones, the *clavicles,* which reach from the sternum out

to the shoulders. There each joins with a flat triangular bone
lying on the upper part of the back. These flat triangular bones,
the *scapulae,* are not joined directly to the spinal column but
lie against the ribs and are attached to them with flat muscles.
The two clavicles and the two scapulae form the *shoulder*

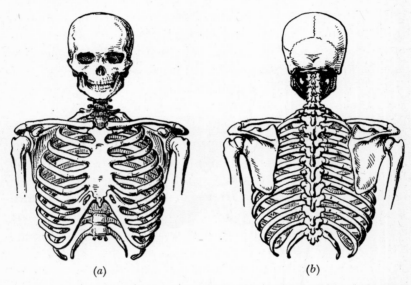

(a)   (b)

FIG. 2. The upper arm bones meet the shoulder girdle to form the shoulder
joints—(*a*) as it looks from the front; (*b*) as it looks from the back.

girdle. This girdle is closed in front, but open in back because
the inner sides of the scapulae do not meet.

At each shoulder the clavicle and scapula are joined in such
a way as to form a circular hollow, and into this hollow is
fitted the top of the long bone of the upper arm (Figure 2).
The lower end of the long bone of the upper arm meets the
two bones of the lower arm at the elbow, and the bones of the
lower arm meet the bones of the hand at the wrist.

Eliminating the details, the basic bony structures of the body
may be drawn in a few lines, as in Figure 3.

Wherever two bones meet, a *joint* is formed. This joint is

tied together with ligaments, muscles and tendons. The *liga-ments* are flat, white, tough pieces of tissue which are attached to both bones of the joint, thus holding them together. These ligaments are not elastic. They may be stretched if sufficient force is used, but they do not return to their original length after the force is removed. Because of this tough nonstretching quality they not only hold the joint firmly together, but they limit the range of movement of the bones at any joint. If one of the bones is forcibly pushed or pulled too far, the ligament may be stretched or torn, and a painful *sprain* results.

The muscles and their tendons which cross a joint also serve to hold it together. *Muscles* are made of many small fibers wrapped together in bundles by thin, white, transparent tissue. These fibers and their covering tissues join together in a strong white band at either end. This white band is the *tendon,* and it attaches the muscle to the bone. The tendons resemble liga-ments in that they do not stretch or shorten but may be torn if too great force is exerted on them. The muscle fibers are elastic, and they shorten and lengthen to move the bones to which they are attached.

The general structure of a joint may be easily understood by examining a chicken joint or a joint of pork, beef, or mutton. Meat is animal muscle, and the construction of the human muscle is the same as that of the animal. The muscle fibers are the tender (or tough) edible portion; the tendons are the white, slippery, cordlike portions; and the ligaments are the smooth, flat, white surfaces which cling tightly to the bones.

Muscles are, in general, arranged in pairs, one of each pair on either side of the joint which they cover. As one muscle of a pair shortens it pulls the bones together on that side, making an angle. In order that the opposing muscle of the pair shall not be torn by this pull, it relaxes and lengthens. This process of alternate shortening and lengthening (*reciprocal innerva-tion*) occurs automatically in the normal muscle and makes it possible for the bones to move easily and freely about the joint.

The *idea* of the paired arrangement of muscles about a joint may be sketched by adding a few lines to the stick figure (Figure 4).

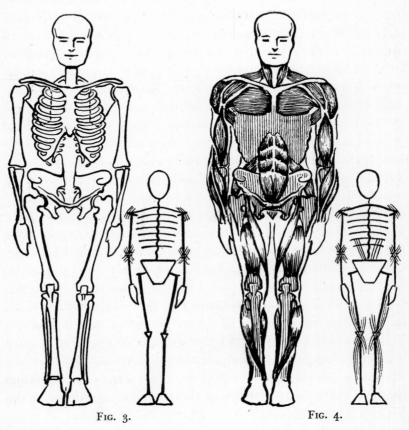

FIG. 3.   FIG. 4.

FIG. 3. The fundamental bony structures of the body may be represented by a few lines.

FIG. 4. The muscles are arranged in pairs around the joints.

At each joint the ends of the bones are shaped in their own peculiar way, fitting together in various patterns. Because of these bony arrangements, it is possible for the bones to move only in certain directions. The ligaments hold them closely together and further limit the amount of motion and the direction of the motion which may take place. The muscles, by contracting and relaxing alternately, cause the bones to move, but because each lengthening muscle can be stretched only so far and because the bulk of the contracting muscle eventually gets in the way of the moving bone, the muscles also serve to limit the amount of motion which may take place at any joint.

The versatility of the joints is as amazing as are their limitations. To understand the complexity, the range, and the limitations of motion in the joints, experiment with your own body. No two persons will have exactly the same range of motion in comparable joints. Each person must move with the joints he possesses, utilizing the possibilities for full range of motion and adapting motion to the limitations of his individual joint structure.

Begin with the hand. It may be closed tightly, each finger bending forward in three distinct places. It may be opened flat out, and the fingers will spread apart or remain close together. The thumb may be brought across the hand until it touches the little finger, it may be moved until it lies along the index finger, or it may be stretched back to form a wide V with the index finger. It may also be moved about so that it makes a full circle around its base. The fingers may be forced back until they form a curve with the back of the hand, but their motion backward is very limited because of the shapes of the bones at the knuckle joints and because of the arrangement of the muscles and tendons which cross the palm to the fingers.

The wrist is very versatile. Hold the right forearm firmly in the left hand and explore the actions of the wrist joint. The whole hand may be moved toward the forearm; it may also be bent backward to about a forty-five-degree angle. The whole hand may be moved toward the thumb side and moved even farther toward the little-finger side. The structure of the wrist joint is such that it is also possible to combine these motions, causing the whole hand to move in a circular fashion.

One of the most interesting and useful motions of which the body is capable is the ability to twist the lower part of the forearm in such a way that the hand may be turned either palm upward or back upward without moving the upper arm. Place the left hand firmly on the right elbow and extend the right hand and forearm palm upward. Without moving the elbow, turn the hand over until the back of it faces upward. Note the diagonal twist which occurs in the forearm as the two bones appear to cross over. Turn the hand back to its palm-upward position, and note that the two bones in the forearm are now parallel. This motion enables the hand to rotate through an arc of 180 degrees from palm up (*supination*) to palm down (*pronation*). This motion is used thousands of times each day and is a part of almost every skill the hand is able to perform.

The action of the elbow joint is simpler and more restricted. The chief action of the elbow is *flexion,* which brings the forearm up until it meets the upper arm. The joint can be straightened until the arm forms a straight line, but motion backward from that straight line is very limited because of the shape of the bones which form the elbow joint. With the arm extended, the elbow joint is locked from side to side, and no motion is possible. If the bony lock is released by bending the elbow slightly, some sideward motion is possible. If the elbow is bent still farther, the flexion may be combined with the pronation of the forearm to move the lower arm across the chest or to raise the hand to the face, or drop it downward in the mid-line of the body.

The shoulder joint operates on a *ball-and-socket* principle. The head of the long bone of the upper arm is shaped like a ball, which fits into a smooth cup-shaped socket formed by the clavicle and the scapula. Within this socket the ball-shaped head turns freely, and the arm is enabled to move in many directions. Its versatility is increased by the slight movement of the clavicle and the wide range of movement of the scapula, to which the armbone is attached by ligaments and tendons.

Raise the arm sideward to shoulder level. Continue raising
it until it touches the head. Move it slightly forward and continue the motion across the face and downward until the arm
has made a full circle. Raise it again until it touches the head
and move it slightly backward. It will continue to move diagonally across the back of the head, but it cannot complete the
circle because the shoulder muscles impede its progress. Raise
the arm forward, upward, and then observe how it rotates in
its socket to move backward and downward, again making a
complete circle. In all the positions the arm may also be turned
outward or inward along its long axis, bringing either the
upper surface or the undersurface forward.

Using the flat muscles of the back, pull the shoulders backward until the edges of the scapulae touch. Using the muscles
of the chest, pull the shoulders forward. Using the muscles
which lie along the top of the shoulder, raise the shoulders
upward, then allow them to drop down below their usual
resting position. Combine all these motions and make a full
circle with the shoulders, forward, then backward.

When these many shoulder-girdle motions are combined with
the motions possible at the elbow, the wrist, the hand, and the
fingers, it becomes possible to place the hands and fingers in
any position within range of the length of the arm. Such diverse
motions as writing, playing the piano, eating, combing the
hair, and fastening buttons can easily be performed. Dozens of
small movements and scores of muscles are involved in the
performance of each of these routine tasks. It seems incredible
that the human mind and body ever learns to perform any of
them successfully; it is even more incredible that once learned
they are performed without conscious thought on the part of
the individual.

The movements of the head and neck should also be explored. Drop the head forward as far as possible, and note the
pull on the muscles of the back of the neck and shoulders.
Bend the neck and head backward, and note that this is a much

more limited motion than forward bending. The bones of the neck impede each other, and the muscles of the throat soon reach their limit of stretch. Bend the head sideward, and note the pull on the muscles on the opposite side of the neck. Twist the head sideward until you can see behind you without turning the body. Rotate the head and neck until they make a complete circle. Considering the large number of positions in which the head may be placed, it is little wonder that many people have difficulty in keeping it balanced firmly upon their shoulders.

The upper back, even though it has many small bones and joints, is a fairly rigid structure. Round it slightly, straighten it slightly—it can perform no other movements. The ribs, which are attached to the vertebrae, impede all other motions. The movements of the shoulder girdle give the upper back the appearance of flexibility, but in reality the range of motion of the spinal column itself is very small.

The motion of the ribs is easy to feel but difficult to describe. The ribs are attached to the vertebrae slantwise and open and close somewhat in the manner of venetian blinds. Place the hands on the ribs and take a deep breath. Feel the bones move upward and outward. Exhale, and feel them collapse to their closed position. Assume an exaggerated military posture with the "chest thrown out." Again inhale and exhale, and note how the movement of the ribs is decreased. Allow the shoulders to slump forward as far as possible. Again inhale and exhale, and note the limited movement of the ribs. Now lift the chest into an easy position with no strain, and again note how easily and freely the ribs move upward and outward, inward and downward. The muscles which control this action are made of short fibers running diagonally between the upper and lower margins of each pair of ribs. As they contract, the ribs are raised. As they relax, the ribs are lowered to the closed position. When the rib cage is held rigid or is cramped into a sunken position, these muscles are impeded in their action, and it becomes impossible to draw a deep breath because the muscles are unable to move the ribs outward to allow the lungs to expand.

The lower back is much more flexible than the upper back and permits of movement forward, backward, sideward, and in a diagonal twist. This greater flexibility is possible both because there are no other bony structures like the ribs to impede the motion and because of slight variations in the shape of the vertebrae to permit greater movement at each of the joints. Contract the abdominal muscles to bend the body forward. Do not allow the body to move at the hip joints, for this will give a false impression of the flexibility of the spinal column. Bend the body backward as far as possible and note the curve which the lower part of the spine assumes. Bend sideward, allowing the hand to drop down the outside of the leg; twist slightly forward and notice how much farther the hand can be moved downward. Stand upright and twist the upper part of the body sideward. This last motion is limited in range but becomes important in many activities.

The motion of the pelvic girdle in relation to the spinal column will be discussed many times in later chapters. It is a complex motion, involving both the lower part of the spinal column and the action of the pelvic girdle at the hip joints. It can be experienced by standing in the upright position and moving the pelvic girdle with the hands. Place the hands across the top of the bony girdle with the thumbs pointing backward and the index fingers resting on the little bony hump at the point where the pelvis slopes sharply downward in front. Press down with the index fingers and up with the thumbs causing the whole girdle to move downward, backward, and upward as it rotates about the hip joint. The curve between the buttocks and the lower back will be greatly increased, giving the appearance of the "shelf-made girl." Now reverse the action. Press down with the thumbs and lift with the fingers, rotating the pelvic girdle down, under, and forward until the tip of the spine curls forward under the body in the whipped-puppy tail-between-the-legs position. Move the pelvic girdle backward and forward between these two positions. Observe the positions in a mirror and be amazed at the difference in your appearance caused by this apparently slight motion. Within a range of motion of less than two inches the body becomes sway-backed, then balanced, and then slumped in a forward curve. Obviously this small motion is one that should be understood and controlled!

The true hip joint may be located by running the fingers along the side of the upper leg bone, digging in with them until the point is found where the top of the leg bone disappears in the socket of the pelvic girdle. This is another ball-and-socket joint, not quite so versatile as that explored in the shoulder but still possessed of a wide range of motions.

With the feet firmly placed on the floor, keep the trunk straight and bend forward from the hips. The body moves around this main hinge until a right angle is formed between the trunk and the legs. If at this point the lower back is allowed to flex, the motion may be continued downward until the hands touch the floor and the head almost touches the knees. Strain on the muscles of the back of the leg will be felt as the body pulls forward. If the knees are relaxed and allowed to bend slightly to relieve this strain, the downward motion may be continued farther. Straighten up and try to bend backward. Some motion is possible, but the range of the motion is greatly limited by the shapes of the bones involved and by the pull of the muscles and ligaments which cross the hip joint in front.

Hold the trunk erect and allow the upper leg to bend forward; note that it is also necessary to bend the knee joint in the opposite direction to maintain balance and to permit the leg muscles, which cross both the hip joint and the knee joint, to contract.

Shifting the weight of the body to one leg, explore the motions of the other leg about the hip joint when it is freed of the limitations imposed upon it by the necessity of supporting the weight of the body. Raise the leg forward. The height to which the leg can be raised is limited by the stretching ability of the muscles which lie along the back of the leg and attach to the pelvic girdle. A dancer may be able to bring his leg up until it touches his body and his head. The untrained person will probably not have such extreme flexibility. The leg may also be swung diagonally upward toward the opposite shoulder, or diagonally upward and outward away from the body. The backward swing is limited by the ligaments which cross the front hinge of the body between the pelvic girdle and the thigh. Swing the leg sideward and outward, then sideward in front of the supporting leg, and sideward in back of the supporting leg. Combine the forward, backward, and sideward motions to allow the leg to make a full circle. In all the positions tried so far, note also that the leg may be rotated or twisted around its own axis. The versatility of the hip joint makes possible walking, running, dancing, swimming, and all activities using the legs; the large number of movements possible also causes many individual variations in the performance of these skills as the various motions are controlled or allowed to occur without relation to the movement intended.

The knee joint, which bears the accumulated weight of the entire trunk and upper leg, is designed for stability. The interlocking bones, ligaments, and muscles of the knee joint permit of very little motion except flexion, or bending. With the legs bearing the weight of the body, bend the knees and note again the synchronized action of the knee and hip joints. Try to straighten the entire leg by throwing the knee joint backward. Note the slight movement possible and the way in which the bones appear to lock rigidly in this backward position. Observe that no sideward motion is possible with the knee joint straight. Raise one foot from the floor to allow the lower leg to move freely. Now it is possible to bend the knee without bending the hip joint. The lower leg may be moved backward and upward until it touches the upper leg. Bend the knee slightly and note that sideward motion of the lower leg becomes possible but is still limited.

The ankle joint, which must bear the entire weight of the body in the standing position, is also very stable, with interlocking bones and strong tendons and ligaments to hold it firm. The lower leg may move forward over the foot, decreasing the angle between the foot and the leg, but this motion is limited by the strong pull of the heel tendons. Raise the foot from the floor, and the ankle joint becomes more movable. Extend the foot until the leg and foot form a straight line; bend the foot back toward the leg until the pull on the heel cord stops the motion. Turn the foot inward and upward, then outward and upward. Combine these motions and the foot will make a full circle about the ankle joint. Any of these motions may occur in walking as the foot is alternately swung forward and placed on the floor to support the weight of the body.

The foot and toes are less agile than the hand and fingers but are possessed of the same motions in lesser degree. Flex the foot by curling the toes under; extend the toes backward toward the top of the foot. Spread the toes and bring them back together again. Try to move the toes one by one, and compare that movement with the movement of the fingers. As compared with the motions possible in the hand, the movements of the foot are relatively slight, but the degree to which those movements are controlled and utilized determines much of the ease, efficiency, and grace of walking.

This cursory survey of the main joints of the body and their movements should serve to emphasize that the body is a highly complex machine with many moving parts capable of many intricate motions. To learn to control all those possible motions, to select those which accomplish a given task, and to eliminate those which are wasted in the performance of that task is not always a simple problem. It is, however, the problem which must be solved if motion is to be economical, efficient, and graceful.

The operation of the paired muscles which surround the principal joints has been reasonably well illustrated in the foregoing experiments in body motion. Certain other muscles have unique characteristics which should also be understood.

The muscles which form the abdominal wall have a complicated set of actions which are of great importance in the normal functioning of the vital systems of the body as well as in the control of all major motions. These muscles have long fibers arranged in flat sheets attached to the margins of the pelvic girdle, the rib cage, and the spinal column. These muscles extend vertically, horizontally, and diagonally from the mid-line downward and from the mid-line upward, providing a muscular girdle which has the ability to stretch and contract in four directions (Figure 5). It is not possible to feel the separate layers of these muscles, but it is possible to feel the action which they impart as they contract and lengthen.

Place the hands flat on the abdomen with the fingers pointing downward and toward the mid-line of the body. Forcibly contract all the abdominal muscles by pulling the abdominal wall

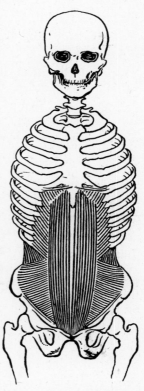

FIG. 5. The abdominal muscles run vertically, horizontally, and diagonally.

in and making the abdomen as thin as possible. This is a concerted action of all four sets of muscles, producing a strong pressure on the abdominal contents. This combined contraction can be held but briefly for it interferes with breathing. Explore the separate motions possible by contracting certain layers more forcibly than others. Twist the body sideward at the waist, noting the diagonal and horizontal pulls. Bend forward at the waist, contracting the abdominal muscles, and note the vertical contraction. Lying on the back, with knees bent to keep the muscles which flex the hip joint from working, raise the trunk (trying to come to a sitting position) and note the strong contraction of the abdominal muscles both vertically and diagonally.

One of the most important functions of these abdominal muscles is to hold the pelvic girdle in position. The muscles are attached to the pelvic girdle along its front and upper margins. By the proper contraction of these muscles, the pelvic girdle can be made to tilt either forward or backward. This tilting process is assisted by the pull of the muscles which form the buttocks, the *gluteal* muscles. The gluteal muscles are attached to the outer surface of the pelvic girdle in back and proceed downward to the upper legs and thighs. When these muscles are contracted, the pelvic girdle rotates about the hip joint so that the end of the spine moves downward and forward.

Place the hands on the pelvic girdle with the thumbs pointing backward and the index fingers resting on the bony hump on the margin of the pelvis, just where it begins to slant sharply downward—the same position used in exploring the motion of the action of the pelvic girdle earlier in this chapter. Again push downward with the index fingers and pull upward with the thumbs to move the pelvic girdle into the extreme tilted position, producing a sway-backed curve with the buttocks protruding noticeably. From this position slowly contract the abdominal muscles, consciously pulling upward toward the ribs, and contract the gluteal muscles, pulling downward and forward until the end of the spine moves down and under and forward into the uptilted position. Take the hands away and reverse the motion, rotating the pelvic girdle so that the tip of the spine moves downward, backward, and upward. Repeat these motions, forward and backward, trying to get the feel of the muscular pulls required. This motion should not be a "sucking in" of the abdominal wall, but an "up in front and down in back—down in front and up in back" pull to move the girdle under the body. The ability to control this forward and backward motion, bringing the pelvic girdle into a balanced position directly under the trunk, is the basis of balanced posture, and this motion is controlled by the action of the abdominal and gluteal muscles. (If this motion proves too difficult in the standing position at first, begin by lying on the back with the knees bent, flattening the back to the floor as the tip of the spine moves forward under the body, allowing the back to hollow as the position is reversed. When the feeling of the muscle pulls is well perceived, try it again in a standing position.)

Another highly important muscle which behaves in a unique manner is the *diaphragm*. It is a conical or dome-shaped muscle which lies above the abdominal viscera and below the heart and lungs. The outer edges of the muscle are attached to the bones of the rib cage, and the muscle fibers run from the edge to the point or dome, which is movable. As the fibers contract, the dome is flattened or pulled downward. This creates more space for the lungs above it, allowing them to expand as a deep breath is taken. As the dome moves downward the space in the abdominal cavity is decreased, and the downward movement of the diaphragm supplies pressure to the abdominal viscera. As the fibers of the diaphragm relax, the dome moves upward and the air is forced from the lungs. This diaphragm muscle is peculiar in that there is no way to exercise it except by breathing, and unless it functions properly, deep breathing is impossible.

All the muscles of the body, whatever their function, are composed of many tiny fibers which resemble slightly stretched rubber bands. They can become shorter, or they can be made to stretch farther. These fibers are each connected with the *central nervous system* of the body and receive impulses and directions from the nervous system. So long as an individual is alive, these fibers are constantly receiving slight impulses from the nervous system, which keep them alert and ready to act. This state of readiness to act is called *tonus,* and it is never completely absent unless the nervous connection with the muscle has been severed. This tonus varies in degree, depending upon the impulses received and the physical state of the muscle. There may be very little tonus, in which case the muscle has little elasticity and becomes flaccid and unwilling to act. There may be too much tonus, keeping the muscle in such a constant state of tension that it becomes fatigued because it can not relax.

The impulses which cause the muscles to contract and relax come from the brain and are carried over the central nervous system. The body also possesses another set of nerve fibers, the *sensory nervous system.* These nerves extend from the eyes, the ears, the nose, the mouth, and the skin to the brain. They convey the impressions received by the five senses to the brain, and through them the brain becomes aware of what is seen, heard, smelled, tasted, or felt. In the brain these stimuli are transferred to the central nervous system and sent back to the muscles, enabling them to respond to the situation which has been perceived. For example, a mosquito buzzes; the ear hears the sound and communicates to the brain the information that a mosquito is near; the brain transfers this information to the central nervous system, which in turn communicates it to the appropriate muscles; these impulses cause the individual to raise an arm and brush the mosquito away.

Through this chain of communication from the senses to the brain to the muscle, all actions of the muscles are controlled. Thus the muscles are always under the control of the brain. This control may be conscious, as when an arm is raised, flexed, extended, and flexed again in an intentional pattern; or it may be semiconscious and appear to be automatic, as when a person walks along giving no conscious thought to the process of locomotion, automatically adjusting the use of the feet and legs to maintain balance even when walking on uneven ground.

The important fact is that muscles are always under the control of the brain. What they do is determined by what their owner wants them to do. A normal individual who is clumsy, awkward, or strained in his movements is clumsy, awkward, or strained because he does not care enough to make the effort to cause his muscles to respond properly with sufficient control and effort to meet the situation. If the desire for efficient movement is strong enough, the brain can be taught to control the muscles in such a way that strong, efficient, and graceful movement will result. Wishful thinking will not do it. The desire for strength, efficiency, and grace must be strong enough to bring about persistent practice until the brain and muscles are trained to respond in the desired manner.

Muscles require food and oxygen to supply them with the energy which they expend in activity. These energy supplies are brought to them by the *circulatory system*. The *heart* is a muscular pump, which, as it contracts and relaxes, pushes the blood out into the arteries. The *arteries* are long tubes made of another kind of muscular tissue, and the blood is sent along through them by the alternate stretching, contracting, and relaxing of the muscular walls. The arteries and their branches conduct the blood to the capillaries. The *capillaries* are very tiny, very thin-walled tubes which lie within the structure of the muscle. There are so many of them and they are arranged in such a way that each tiny muscle fiber is in direct contact with one or more capillaries. Through the thin walls of the capillaries the oxygen and food of the blood stream pass directly to the muscle fiber. In exchange, the blood stream receives the carbon dioxide and fatigue products of the muscle and carries them off for disposal and conversion into fresh energy supplies. Through this exchange the muscle fiber is refreshed and given new energy to carry on its work of contraction.

As the blood passes through the capillaries it reaches the veins, which conduct it back to the lungs and the heart. The *veins* are thin-walled tubes, very poorly supplied with muscle fibers. The force which the pumping action of the heart applied to move the blood along has all been spent, but the veins must return the blood to the heart nevertheless. This problem of venous return is made more complex by the fact that much of the blood must flow uphill, against the downward pull of gravity, to reach the heart. This uphill return is possible only because the veins are fitted with one-way *valves,* which open to permit the blood to flow toward the heart and then close to prevent it from slipping back toward the muscles from which it has come. As the muscle fibers, between which the capillaries and small veins pass, contract, they become shorter and thicker and squeeze the blood from the capillaries and small veins. Since the one-way valves permit the blood to move in only one direction, the blood is squeezed into the veins. As the muscle fibers relax, the capillaries are again filled with blood from the arterial branches. This alternate squeezing and opening process forces the blood along in the direction of the heart.

The small veins join together and form larger veins, and eventually the blood from all parts of the body reaches the large veins which run through the *abdominal cavity.* This abdominal cavity is surrounded by a muscular wall and closed at the top by the diaphragm, which lies flat above the abdominal viscera and is attached to the bony margins of the rib cage. When a breath is inhaled the diaphragm moves down and exerts pressure on the abdominal cavity. This pressure squeezes the large veins and forces the blood upward into the veins of the *thoracic cavity* (the chest), which has become larger and roomier as the diaphragm moved downward. As the breath is exhaled, the diaphragm again moves upward, decreasing the size of the thoracic cavity, exerting pressure on the veins, and squeezing the blood onward in its return to the heart. At the same time the abdominal pressure is decreased, and more blood enters the large veins from the small veins which feed them.

This pumping process can proceed efficiently only if the muscular walls of the abdominal cavity are strong and in good condition. If these walls are weak and flabby, the pressure exerted by the diaphragm only serves to push the front of the abdomen outward, and little pressure is exerted on the abdominal veins. These veins are very large and may contain at times as much as half the total blood supply of the entire body. If the pressure-pumping system is inefficient, much of this blood remains in the abdominal veins and only a small quantity is returned to the heart. The heart cannot send out blood which it does not receive, so less energy-carrying blood is sent out to the muscles. The muscles receive a decreased oxygen and food supply and are unable to rid themselves of their fatigue products. The semistarved muscles cannot refresh themselves and become fatigued. Eventually this fatigue becomes chronic, and the whole body feels tired and listless, or tired and tense. Less blood is sent to the arteries going to the head, and the brain is deprived of oxygen. The starved brain does not function efficiently, and a feeling of dizziness or lightheadedness may result. Much of the total well-being of the body depends upon the efficiency of the veins and abdominal pumping system, and much of this efficiency is determined by the kind and amount of exercise which these systems receive.

When blood has been returned to the heart through the veins, it is immediately sent out to the lungs to rid itself of the fatigue gases which it has taken from the muscles, so that a new load of oxygen may be taken on for delivery to the muscles. This oxygenated blood returns to the heart and then begins its journey to the muscles as described above. The lungs, therefore, play a very necessary part in the dynamics of body action by bringing to the blood stream the oxygen which the muscles use to transform their fuel into energy.

The biochemistry of what occurs in the muscle as it uses

oxygen to convert its fuel into energy is a long and involved story. A simple explanation of the process can be given by likening the conversion of muscle fuel into energy with the similar process of burning coal to produce heat and energy. Coal will burn only when it is supplied with oxygen. Open the drafts on the furnace and the smoldering coal bursts into flame, heat is given off, and the smoke carrying the end products of this combustion goes up the chimney. As the energy of the coal is exhausted, more coal must be added to keep the fire burning. Close the drafts so that no additional air reaches the coal and the smoke cannot go up the chimney; the fire is soon extinguished, and neither heat nor energy can be obtained from the coal. Similarly in the muscle, the arteries are the drafts which bring fresh supplies of oxygen. They are also the firemen in that they bring fresh food supplies for fuel. The veins are the chimney which carry off the fatigue products. When both are working properly, the muscle burns its fuel to give off heat and the energy which enables it to contract. When either is "closed" the muscle soon becomes inert and unable to carry on its energy-liberating function.

The *lungs* are made up of many tiny elastic *sacs,* joined together and opening inward toward the air passage from the nose and mouth. The lungs resemble a large sponge, made up of many tiny balloons. As a sponge increases in size when water is poured into it, so the lungs increase in size when air enters the tiny sacs and expands them. These sacs are in direct contact with many capillaries of the circulatory system. As the blood in the capillaries reaches the expanded sacs, which are filled with air, the oxygen from the air passes through the walls to the blood in the capillaries. At the same time the carbon dioxide in the blood passes through the walls and enters the lung sacs to be exhaled. By this exchange the blood is constantly giving up fatigue products and taking on fresh oxygen to carry to the muscles to enable them to continue their work.

The lungs are protected from external harm by the rib cage,

which is made up of the spinal column, the ribs, and the flat bone to which the ribs are attached in front (the sternum). The ribs are attached to the spinal column with joints which act as hinges. Between each pair of ribs are strips of muscle running diagonally. As these muscles contract, they raise the ribs and tend to turn the lower borders outward, so that the whole rib cage becomes larger. This increase in the size of the rib cage decreases the pressure in the lungs, and air rushes in from the nose and the mouth. As the muscles relax, the ribs return to their resting position and in so doing push the air out of the lungs. The action of the diaphragm is synchronized with that of the ribs, so as the ribs move out the diaphragm moves down, and as the ribs return to their original position, the diaphragm moves upward, helping to push the air out of the lungs.

By these alternating movements of the ribs and diaphragm the air in the lungs is changed with each breath; air laden with the fatigue gases taken from the blood stream is pushed out, and fresh, oxygen-carrying air is taken in to be transferred to the blood stream. When the body is moving vigorously, the blood flows more rapidly, and breathing becomes faster and deeper to keep up with the job of removing the fatigue gases and providing fresh oxygen for the working muscles.

The muscles which control breathing must be in good condition to contract and relax quickly over their full range of motion. If this free motion is interfered with in any way, the air supply to the lungs and the removal of the fatigue gases from the blood stream are decreased. If the chest is allowed to collapse in a sunken-in position with the shoulders forward and the abdomen protruding, the rib cage becomes a prison for the lungs and the heart, impeding their action and making them less and less efficient. This situation is not remedied by taking ten deep breaths and then allowing the chest to collapse again, for there is no way in which oxygen can be stored in the body for future use. A steady supply of oxygen and a steady removal of carbon dioxide is needed at all times, and these needs can be readily met only if the breathing muscles are kept in good condition and the rib cage is carried in such a way as to free the heart and lungs for their normal function. If the ribs are collapsed, the diaphragm is also crowded. Then it cannot move upward and downward as it should, and this interferes with the return of blood from the abdominal veins as well as with breathing.

To free the heart, lungs, and diaphragm for adequate functioning, the rib cage must be able to move freely, so that nothing interferes with the easy action of the muscles in raising and lowering the ribs. In this position, the lungs expand naturally and easily, the heart is uncrowded, and the diaphragm can move easily upward and downward.

The fuel which the muscles burn comes from the food which is eaten. The food is carried to the *stomach* and *intestines,* where it is digested and converted into blood sugar. This blood sugar is stored in the *liver*. The blood sugar is transferred from the liver to the blood stream as it is needed by the muscles, carried to the muscles by the circulatory system, and in the muscles it is burned as fuel to provide energy to move the muscles. The parts of the food which cannot be utilized as fuel continue to move down the intestinal tract and eventually are excreted as waste material. Thus the *digestive system* has two functions; it changes food into fuel which can be burned by the muscles, and it eliminates the waste materials which remain after the food has been converted into fuel.

The *digestive tract* is made up of hollow tubes with strong muscular walls. These muscular walls contract and relax and by these motions churn the food and push it along. These muscular walls must be kept in good condition and tone if they are to perform this function. When food enters these tubes, the walls are stretched by the pressure of the food. If the muscle fibers are in good condition they resist this stretching by contracting, and this contraction pushes the food along. As the food moves forward, the walls of the tube relax, and more food is pushed in. This alternate stretching, contracting, and relaxing moves the food along through the body and eventually forces the waste materials out of the body. If the muscular walls of the digestive tract are weak, flabby, or stretched out of shape, they are like a piece of elastic which has lost its snap. They do not resist the further stretching as food is forced into the tubes, little if any contraction occurs, and the food remains stationary or is moved along very slowly.

The condition of the digestive muscle fibers and the efficiency of the digestive process is determined by several factors. The blood supply to the several parts of the digestive tract must be adequate. The soft digestive tubes must be held in position so that they do not sag and pull downward. And the abdominal wall must be firm and strong to help resist the stretching which occurs when food enters the intestines.

The abdomen is not protected and enclosed by a bony cage. The spine protects it in back; the pelvic girdle forms a partial support below; the diaphragm pushes down on it from above; and the front wall is composed of the layers of the abdominal muscles. The shape of the abdominal cavity and the pressures exerted on its contents may be changed by the movement of any of these four enclosing surfaces. If the pelvic girdle is tilted so that the tip of the spine points backward and upward, the intestines are deprived of support from beneath and the abdomen sags downward. This permits the intestines to sag against the front wall, and they are stretched and pulled out of their normal position. If the pelvic girdle is tilted in the opposite direction, so that the end of the spine curves too far forward under the body, the abdominal contents are crowded up against the diaphragm. But if the pelvic girdle is balanced properly, the abdominal contents rest easily in the bony basin and there is no sagging or pulling on the intestinal walls. This balanced position of the pelvis is maintained by controlled use of the abdominal and gluteal muscles. Exercise which improves the functioning and control of these muscles is an aid to the process of digestion.

If the abdominal muscles are lax and stretched they provide poor support in front for the intestinal tract. The intestines push outward against this weak wall, and little resistance is offered to encourage the contraction of the intestines and the moving of food and waste along the tract. The slow and inefficient movement of the food through the intestines allows the food to stagnate and ferment, further distending the intestinal walls. The push against the abdominal muscles is increased, these muscles are stretched farther, and the whole abdominal wall protrudes and sags downward. Partly digested food accumulates in the intestinal tract, elimination is poor, gas is formed which further interferes with the digestive process, the abdomen protrudes, and the well-being of the individual is decreased because digestion is inefficient. To counteract this sagging condition, the muscular walls of the abdominal cavity must be toned and made strong and firm so that they can apply normal resistance to the stretching of the intestines, encouraging the normal passage of food and waste materials through them. Strong abdominal muscles are as important to the digestive process as they are to the circulatory process; abdominal exercise plays an important part in keeping the whole body in good functional condition.

This chapter has described in a somewhat cursory fashion the basic structures of the body which are involved in movement and exercise. It should be studied carefully to provide a basis for understanding the principles of motion and exercise which are discussed in later chapters.

PROJECTS FOR FURTHER STUDY

1. When you have chicken or other fowl for dinner, carefully examine one of the joints in the leg or wing. Identify the muscles,

tendons, and ligaments. Note how they are arranged to hold the joint together and to initiate and limit the motion in the joint. Move the two bones which meet to form the joint, noting how the muscles on one side (the agonists) must shorten to initiate the movement, while the muscles on the opposite side (the antagonists) resist the movement and must lengthen to make it possible.

2. Compare your right hand with the right hand of a friend. Spread the fingers as far as possible. Flex the fingers. Extend the fingers backward. Flex the wrist. Extend it backward. Compare the range of motion in each action in the two hands. Can all persons perform the same motions with equal ease?

3. Place your hands flat over your ribs. Breathe deeply and let the air out slowly. Note the way in which the ribs move up and out, then in and down. Compare this action with the motion of venetian blinds.

4. Standing, contract your abdominal muscles as strongly as you can to "suck in" the abdominal wall. Hold this position as long as you can. Why is it uncomfortable? Still standing, use your thumbs as described on page 24 to move your pelvic girdle into the balanced position, giving maximum support to the abdominal contents. Hold this position as long as you held the first position. Is it more comfortable? Why?

Part II

THE EXPENDITURE OF ENERGY

CHAPTER

3

The Uses of Exercise

EXERCISE IS body movement. Any motion performed by the body or any of its parts is exercise. The beating of the heart, the movement of the ribs in breathing, the contractions of the muscles necessary to hold the body in an erect position, the arm swing which propels a tennis racket through the air, the small finger movements which push the keys of a typewriter down—all are exercise. Muscle tissue contracts, relaxes, or stretches; energy is expended; work is done. The muscle action keeps the body alive, affects the feelings of the individual, alters the condition of the muscle itself, or accomplishes some external objective. In a word, exercise is life itself, for it characterizes every living moment.

There are many kinds of exercise, each of which produces its own effects. The effect may be principally upon the skeletal muscles—the voluntary muscles which are attached to the bones and cause them to move; or the effect may be principally upon the *involuntary* muscular tissue of the digestive and respiratory systems. These effects themselves will differ in relation to the kind of exercise used.

The same exercise or motion may be performed in a variety of ways. The motion may be slow, or it may be rapid; it may be easy and languid, or it may be forceful and executed with tension; it may be small, or it may be large in the area covered.

39

Swing the right arm to experience the feeling of the same motion done in a variety of ways. Allow it to move slowly back and forth in an easy arc; then increase the speed of the swing until it is moving as rapidly as possible. Swing it first slowly and then rapidly, keeping the whole arm relaxed; then tense the muscles of the arm and move it vigorously, with all the force that it can exert. Swing the arm easily so that the hand moves only two or three inches; then swing it upward and backward as far as possible. The feeling which the body experiences is different for each variety of this same motion. The purposes of such movements would differ; so also do their effects on the body.

In each kind of exercise, energy is expended, an effect or a result is produced. If energy is spent to produce a result which was neither needed or desired, that energy has been wasted. The physically educated individual chooses the kind of movement which will produce the desired effect with a minimum expenditure of energy. To do this, it is necessary to understand the characteristics of the many types of motion or exercise possible so that an intelligent selection of the right kind for a given situation can be made.

Exercise can be used to strengthen muscle; it can also be used to weaken muscle. Exercise can increase the tension in a muscle; it can also relax or decrease the tension in a muscle. Exercise can increase the rate of heartbeat and raise the blood pressure; it can also cause the heart to beat more slowly and the blood pressure to decrease. Exercise can stimulate and "pep up"; it can fatigue and depress; or it can relax and soothe.

If muscles are too weak to perform the tasks assigned to them, they may be *strengthened*. Muscles are strengthened by causing them to contract forcibly, or by causing them to contract against a resisting force. This strengthening process cannot be accomplished overnight. It must be done gradually and consistently over a period of time. Each day the muscles must be required to work as hard as they are able for a period of time, and day by day the work required of them must be increased. The amount of work may be increased by performing the exercise for a longer period each day; it may be increased by doing the exercise more rapidly; or it may be made more strenuous by increasing the amount of resistance.

The classic example of the development of strength through gradually increasing the resistance and the amount of work performed is the story of the little old lady and her cow. There was no water near the cottage in which they lived; but at the top of the hill was a lake of fresh water. So every day the little old lady picked the cow up in her arms and carried it up the hill to give it a drink. This seems impossible, but the little old lady explained it by saying, "When the cow was a little calf it was so weak it could not walk up the hill. I could lift it then, so I carried it. I carried it every day. The calf grew bigger and bigger, but I became stronger. Now it is a big cow but I am stronger, so I still carry it with ease." The story may or may not be true, but it does illustrate the basic principles for the development of muscular strength.

Exercise will increase the strength of a muscle only if (1) it is intense enough to cause the muscle to work at its maximum level of ability; (2) it is repeated persistently over a period of time; and (3) its demands on the muscle are gradually increased by increasing the number of times the movement is performed, the speed with which the movement is executed, or the resistance against which the movement is performed. Exercises which can be used to increase the strength of specific groups of muscles are described in the Appendix. Good examples of exercises for strength are Nos. 5 to 16.

If muscles are too strong, they can be *weakened;* but this is seldom a necessary or desirable procedure for the normal individual. A muscle can be weakened by decreasing the amount of exercise it receives, giving it less than the amount to which it is accustomed. This weakening of muscles often occurs when a person changes his exercise habits and discontinues some type of activity. It also occurs when a limb is immobilized in a cast or carried in a sling to allow healing of a sprain, strain, or broken bone. The activity of the muscle is interfered with; the blood supply is decreased by this lack of activity; and the muscle gradually loses tone and becomes weaker. When the bandage is taken off and the muscle is again free to move, it must be gradually strengthened by exercise, beginning with easy motion suited to its weakened state and gradually increasing the amount and intensity until it regains its former ability.

If a muscle is too short, so that it impedes free and easy motion of any part of the body, it may be *stretched*. This stretching process must be done very gradually. It is accomplished by forcibly pulling the muscle beyond its resting length, allowing it to return to its resting position, and then pulling it gently but forcibly out to a greater length. If this process is carried on too rapidly or too great force is exerted, the muscle fibers may be torn, so it is essential that stretching of a muscle be done very gradually and persistently over a period of time.

The dancer spends many tedious hours on this stretching process, each day bending forward a little farther, lifting her leg a little higher, increasing the range of movement in the trunk, to increase her flexibility and enable her to move easily, gracefully, and with a wider range of motions. The person who has carried his shoulders forward in a hunched position for such a long time that the muscles extending from the shoulders to the chest wall have become shortened might also use this stretching kind of exercise to gradually lengthen the shoulder-chest muscles so that his shoulders will be comfortable in a balanced position. The heel cord sometimes becomes shortened, making walking painful and awkward. It, too, may gradually be increased in length by persistently stretching it, thus freeing the foot for easier walking. Good examples of stretching exercises are Nos. 1 to 4; 23 to 29; 41, 42, 45, and 46.

Sometimes muscles become stretched by faulty use until they are unable to support a body part in its correct position. Proper exercise will increase the tone and strength of such muscles, gradually *shortening* them until they can perform their proper function with ease. Again, this is not a process which can be accomplished in five minutes; it may be accomplished gradually over a period of time by persistent and correct exercise of the muscles involved.

The most conspicuous example of overstretched muscles is seen in the person who has carried his head forward, allowing it to droop downward for months or years. The muscles which extend from the base of the skull down the neck and out to the shoulders become chronically fatigued, gradually stretch, and are at last unable to hold the head comfortably in the erect position. Vigorous contractions of these muscles will tend to improve their tone and strength, gradually restoring them to their normal length, increasing their ability to hold the head where it belongs. Examples of these and other "shortening" exercises are Nos. 13, 14, 15, 16, 30, and 43.

If muscles are too tense, they may be *relaxed* by exercise. The motion of overtense muscles is awkward and jerky. The tense muscle fibers are in a constant state of partial contraction. In any motion the flexing muscles tend to shorten too rapidly and the opposing muscles are unable to relax easily and completely to allow the motion to be performed smoothly. The overtense fibers may be relaxed by gently stretching them out of their shortened position. This stretching process must be slow, easy, and alternated with periods of allowing the stretched muscle to "give" slightly and return to its shortened position. This alternating stretch and give releases the tension in the fibers and reduces the pressure on the capillaries which was produced by the shortened, cramped muscle fibers. As the pressure on the capillaries is reduced, more blood is allowed to enter, the fatigue products are removed, and fresh oxygen is supplied to the fatigued muscle fiber. As the physical condition of the muscle fiber is improved by this increased blood supply, it becomes rested and relaxed. If this stretching is done too abruptly or too forcibly, the muscle fibers resist the pull and become more tense, increasing the feeling of fatigue and irritability. Exercises of this type are Nos. 1 to 4, 29, 32, and 35 to 39. The problem of relaxation is discussed in much greater detail in Chapter 4.

A muscle may have sufficient strength for the performance of its normal tasks but because of lack of use, laziness on the part of its owner, or inactivity for any reason may tend to become flaccid and lose its tone. Its response to the impulses which come to it over the nervous system becomes sluggish and unco-ordinated. Exercise may be used to *increase the activity* of the muscle, *increase its circulation,* and generally *stimulate it* to a more ready response to the commands of the nervous system. Such exercise should be rapid and free-moving and demand a coordinated response from the muscle. The effect of this kind of exercise is experienced by the person who, though normally active, has been inactive for a period of time. After a game of tennis or golf or a long swim, he feels refreshed by the activity. The same physical effect—though not necessarily the same psychological effect—may be achieved by using any "artificial" exercise requiring arm and leg swings and big movements of the trunk. These exercises are more satisfying if they are rhythmic, the arms and legs moving through a set pattern which is rapidly repeated. This kind of exercise must be sufficiently vigorous to produce an increase in the rate and depth of breathing and the rate of heartbeat and to have the general effect of "stirring up" the body, changing the state of body functioning from one of lethargy to one of activity. Examples of exercises for general stimulation and improvement of muscle tone are Nos. 23 to 25, 28, 31, 33, and 34.

If the person unused to strenuous exercise "overdoes" in an occasional spurt of activity, the fatigue following may be painful and irritating rather than relaxing and refreshing. The unaccustomed body approaches a state of exhaustion, the over-strained muscles are stiff and aching, and the period of recovery from the activity is prolonged. For any exercise program the first rule is "Easy does it," or "Too little is better than too much." The heart, arteries, veins, and muscles that have been functioning at a low level must be *gradually* conditioned for increased activity by increasing the demands made upon them bit by bit. The process cannot be hurried or a short cut found by pushing the body to the point of exhaustion.

The effects of exercise on the internal systems of the body—circulation, respiration, digestion, and elimination—also vary in relation to the type of exercise used. All these systems function by the contraction and relaxation of muscular tissue, different from the large muscles which move the bones but still subject to the same principles.

The arteries and veins cannot be exercised *directly* by instructing them to contract and relax. They can be exercised *indirectly* by using the skeletal muscles and increasing the demand upon the circulatory system for increased circulation to the skeletal muscles. Any strenuous activity which requires large movements of the arms, legs, or trunk increases the rate of the heartbeat and eventually the force of the heartbeat. This increased activity causes the arteries and veins to stretch farther and contract more strongly, more blood passes through them in the same period of time, and more blood is returned to the heart for further delivery, causing it also to stretch farther and contract with greater force. This exercises the muscular tissues of the heart, arteries, and veins, and—if they are in a healthy condition—they will respond to this exercise by becoming stronger and more elastic. They are then in condition to respond to any reasonable demand which may be placed upon them, and when an emergency arises which demands that the person move very rapidly or exert great effort quickly, the circulatory system is ready and able to meet the emergency demand.

Three principal factors, each of which is affected by exercise, affect the workings of the circulatory system: (1) The muscular walls of the heart and arteries themselves must be in good condition so that they may stretch and relax easily to send the blood to the muscles. (2) The muscles which surround the capillaries and small veins must be in good tone to alternately apply pressure and release from pressure to the capillaries to squeeze the blood along in the veins, but the muscle fibers must not be so tense that they squeeze the capillaries too tightly without allowing them to relax long enough to take on new blood. (3) The muscular walls of the abdominal cavity must be strong enough to resist the downward pressure of the diaphragm without stretching so that the pressure in the abdominal cavity will be increased sufficiently to force the blood in the large veins upward to the thoracic cavity and on to the heart.

Corresponding to these three factors are three types of exercise which affect the functioning of the circulatory system. (1) Exercise which is rapid and free-moving and uses the arms, legs, and trunk in large motions stimulates the action of the heart and arteries and helps to improve the tone of the muscles. (2) Exercise which reduces muscular tension by relaxing fatigued and overtense muscle fibers frees the capillaries and increases their ability to carry blood to the muscle fibers. (3) Exercise which strengthens the muscles of the abdominal wall and helps to control their action facilitates the return of blood from the large abdominal veins to the heart, making the blood supply more readily available for the demands of activity. Examples of the first type are Nos. 23, 26, 28, and 31 to 34; of the second type, Nos. 1 to 4; and of the third type, Nos. 5 to 9, 11, 12, 13*b*, 17, 18, 20, and 22.

In a similar manner, the muscles which control respiration may be affected indirectly by exercise. Again, any rapid, free-moving activity which causes the large muscles of the body to contract rapidly increases the demands upon the respiratory system. The chest wall moves up and down more rapidly, and the depth of breathing is increased. This automatic increase in rate and depth of breathing exercises the rib muscles and diaphragm. This strenuous exercise improves their tone and condition, enabling them to respond more readily to any demands the body may make on them. Examples of this kind of exercise are Nos. 28, 31, and 33.

At this point a comment about artificial "deep-breathing exercises" is in order. Conscious deep breathing may be used to stretch the muscles of the chest wall by forcing the ribs to their limit of movement. Such forced breathing, however, has no value in increasing the supply of oxygen to the blood stream and muscle tissues. The body is so wonderfully synchronized that the need for oxygen in the tissues and the rate of delivery of oxygen by the lungs and blood stream is automatically regulated. A muscle fiber will take up additional oxygen only when the need for additional oxygen exists, and this need automatically increases the available supply in the normal, healthy circulatory system. The additional oxygen which is taken into the lungs in forced breathing is not transferred to the blood stream or the muscle fibers unless a deficit exists at that moment. Oxygen cannot be stored away for future use. It is held in the lungs for the moment and then expelled with the next exhalation. Thus, while forced breathing serves to stretch the muscles of the chest wall and force the diaphragm to contract, it serves no other useful purpose. The stretching which is induced could be brought about more naturally by running, jumping, or swinging the arms to increase the demand for oxygen, thus forcing the lungs to breathe more deeply to meet the need.

It should also be noted that forced deep breathing causes many individuals to become dizzy. Since it is an artificial exchange of oxygen and carbon dioxide unrelated to the needs of the body, the balance of oxygen and carbon dioxide necessary to the normal functioning of the body may be disturbed and the circulation temporarily decreased. This produces a state of partial anemia and oxygen hunger in the brain, causing the feeling of dizziness.

Deep-breathing exercises were once a part of all exercise programs, because of the belief that they increased the oxygen supply to all parts of the body. Modern science has shown that this belief has no basis in fact, and modern physiology shows clearly that forced-breathing exercises have no place in the exercise program of the normal individual.

The habitual position of the chest and rib cage also affects the ease and efficiency of respiration. The extreme military "chest out" position makes the rib cage rigid and interferes with normal breathing. The sunken chest which accompanies the round-shoulder position is cramped in its movement, and energy is wasted in raising it from its sunken position to the position in which it is possible for the ribs to move outward. The normal efficient position of the chest and shoulders is discussed in some detail in the chapters dealing with the balanced posture.

The muscular fibers which make up the walls of the tubes of the digestive tract receive their exercise daily, hourly, as food is forced down them to be digested and moved along. *Digestion* is a form of unconsciousness and pleasant exercise. Indirectly it can be affected by exercise of other muscles. The turning, twisting, and squeezing action on the contents of the abdominal cavity which occurs when the arms, legs, and trunk are moved assists the intestinal muscle fibers in the work of churning, squeezing, and pushing the food along to make room for the next meal. The rapid, free-moving activities which stir up a sluggish circulation increase the appetite and the enjoyment of food and thus aid in its digestion. But most important in normal digestion is the kind of exercise which strengthens the muscle layers of the abdominal wall, making them firm and resistant to the stretching of the intestines as the food moves along. Exercises which aid digestion are described in Nos. 19

to 24. The specific application of exercise to the relief of constipation is discussed in Chapter 5.

No discussion of the uses of exercises would be complete without emphasizing the fact that all effects of exercise are *transient*. A muscle fiber is strengthened by appropriate daily exercise. The minute those exercises are discontinued and the muscle is allowed to rest or to return to its former state of inactivity, the strength acquired by exercise begins to be lost. Some will be lost each day, until eventually the muscle reaches the minimum strength which it needs to perform the maximum task demanded of it. It can again be brought to greater strength by exercise, but it will not maintain for any period of time greater strength than it is required to exert. A muscle will not maintain an emergency store of strength for any length of time unless it is periodically required to work harder than it normally does in the performance of its daily activities. This balance between demand and ability is the basis of the need for planned exercise.

This strength in excess of immediate need is important for at least two reasons. First, no person can predict exactly the emergency demands which may be made upon him, when a little extra strength will make the difference between being able or not able to do a piece of work, to lift a weight, or to save a life. Second, the possession of strength in excess of the immediate demands of a job makes the performance of a job easier. If every muscle fiber must be contracted to its maximum to perform a given task, the fibers soon become fatigued. If the fibers are stronger, they may work in relays. Part of them will suffice to do the job, while other fibers rest and restore their energy. As the working fibers tire they may be replaced by fresh ones, while they in turn rest and relax. If the muscle fibers are strong enough to use this relay system, the work may be continued over a longer period of time without undue fatigue.

This strength in excess of daily needs comes from deliberate exercise which causes the muscles to work at their maximum, pushing the maximum a little higher each day. It may be supplied by sports, games, and participation in pleasurable recreational activity for many people. It can also be acquired by the planned use of specific exercise by those people whose daily routine is sedentary, with no occasion for hard muscular work.

Not only strength, but all other results of exercise are transient. A muscle which has been stretched from a shortened position will return to its shortened position unless it is habitually used in its stretched position to maintain its new length. A muscle which was tense and has been relaxed by exercise will gradually return to its tense state unless the process of relaxation is continued or the condition which caused tension is removed. The heart, arteries, and veins which have been toned by exercise will gradually return to their flabby state when activity is discontinued and fewer demands are made on the circulatory system. The abdominal wall which has been flattened and strengthened by exercise will gradually stretch and weaken unless the muscles are habitually used in their controlled position.

At first this seems very discouraging. It would appear that man must spend all of his time in exercise if he is to maintain a condition of healthy fitness for the work he does and the play he enjoys. Literally, of course, this is true. Every living moment is spent in exercise of some kind. The physically educated person merely selects the kind of exercise he will use, adapts the exercise which is incidental to his daily work and play, and performs the normal acts of living in such a manner that the desirable effects of exercise result. When these results are inadequate for any reason, he then selects additional exercise to meet the specific need which is not being met and adds it to his normal daily exercise to correct or improve the functioning of his body. By intelligently utilizing the necessary exercise which accompanies the activity of living, most of the needs of the body can be met. Additional, unusual, emergency, or temporary needs can be met by specific exercises adapted to those specific demands. Both kinds of exercise are discussed in the chapters which follow.

PROJECTS FOR FURTHER STUDY

1. *a.* Sitting quietly on the floor, count your pulse for thirty seconds.
   b. Perform Exercise No. 35. Count your pulse again.
   c. Perform Exercise No. 16 for fifteen seconds. Count your pulse again.
   d. Perform Exercise No. 33 for thirty seconds. Count your pulse again.
   Comment on the effect of exercise on the heart rate.
2. *a.* Lying on your back, legs extended, hands clasped behind your head, come up to a sitting position and return to the floor three times.
   b. Lying on your back, legs extended, arms extended overhead, swing the arms forward vigorously and come up to a sitting position and return to the floor three times.
   c. Perform Exercise No. 11 three times.
   In each exercise the body moved from a lying to a sitting posision. Did all three exercises feel the same? Which one made the strongest use of the abdominal muscles?
3. *a.* Standing, knees locked, quickly bend forward and touch your hands to the floor. Where did you feel the pull? What happened to your abdominal wall?
   b. Standing, knees relaxed, abdominal muscles contracted, perform Exercise No. 3.
   Could you bend farther the second time? Why? Was it easier? Why?
4. *a.* Standing, arms at side, stiffen your arms and fingers as much as possible. Rapidly raise your stiff arms sideward, stopping exactly at the level of the shoulders. Bring your arms rapidly to the starting position, stopping just before your arms touch your sides.

b. Standing, arms at side and relaxed, easily raise your arms
sideward to shoulder level. Let them drop to the starting position.

In each exercise the arms were raised from the sides to shoulder
level and returned. Did both exercises feel the same? What accounts for the difference?

5. Perform Exercise No. 31 as many times as you can in twenty
   seconds. Compare your record with that made by someone else.
   What might account for any difference?

6. Ask a dancer, a high jumper, or a hurdler what she or he does
   to increase the range of motion in the hip joints. Try the exercise. Where do you feel the pull?

7. Sitting quietly, count the number of times you breathe in and
   out in one minute. Forcibly inhale and exhale as deeply as possible ten times. Again count your respirations for one minute.
   What is the effect of deep breathing unaccompanied by activity?

8. List ten situations in which you might need more strength or
   endurance than you usually need for carrying on your daily
   activities. How might you acquire that much strength or endurance?

CHAPTER

4

Exercise and Relaxation

THE PHYSICALLY educated person knows how to expend energy efficiently to accomplish maximum useful results with a minimum amount of effort. This is another way of saying that the physically educated person knows how to conserve energy by using the least possible amount of energy to achieve a given result, eliminating the unnecessary motions and muscle contractions which fatigue him without accomplishing any useful purpose. The tense individual continually wastes energy in meaningless and nonproductive muscle contractions which serve only to fatigue him further and increase his tension; the relaxed individual controls his energy expenditure by permitting only those muscle contractions which serve some useful purpose.

The body responds to the stimulus of fear, or anger, or excitement of any kind by getting ready to act. The heart beats faster, breathing is more rapid, energy-providing substances are released into the blood stream, and the nerves carry a rapid succession of stimuli to the muscles to increase their tonus and incite them to action. This whole response compares with the response which an automobile engine makes when someone "steps on the gas." The engine runs faster and faster. If the brakes are released and the car is thrown into high gear, the car runs down the road at great speed and the increased energy

53

is used to move the car more rapidly. But if the brakes are not
released, or if the car is left in low gear, the engine races and
energy is wasted. So it is with the body. If this potential energy
is released in overt action, it finds a normal outlet as the individual runs away from the thing he fears, fights the thing which
has angered him, or jumps up and down to express his excitement. But modern man is "civilized." He cannot always run
when he is afraid or fight when he is angry, so the racing
"engine" finds no natural outlet for its energy.

The stimulus to physical action occurs in response to the
irritating situation, but the normal response is inhibited by the
individual's submission to the conventional pattern of civilized
living. The two sets of stimuli—the first to act, the second to
inhibit action—are conflicting. The muscles which would exe-
cute the "natural" act are tense in response to the stimulus for
action; the antagonistic muscles are tense in response to the
civilized stimulus to inhibit the natural act. With the paired
opposing muscles both under tension, easy freedom of movement is lost.

The muscles around each joint are arranged in pairs. As one
of a pair contracts, the other must relax and "give" with the
joint movement. If the opposing muscle is under tension, it
tends to resist the movement caused by the acting muscle, and
the normal smooth coordination of the paired muscles is lost,
as the already shortened acting muscle must contract more
forcibly to overcome the resistance of the opposing muscle.
Energy is wasted by the opposing muscle in resisting the movement, and additional energy is spent by the acting muscle to
overcome the resistance. Under these conditions the body loses
the ability to regulate the amount of energy required to perform a given task, and movements are either made too forcibly
or fall short of their mark.

For example, the hand reaches for a glass of water, but the
motion is jerky and the water splashes as the hand attempts to
stop too quickly. Energy was wasted in acceleration of move-

ment; additional energy was wasted in deceleration or slowing of movement. The glass is set down on the table with a jolt, and again the water splashes. The hand has lost the ability to coordinate all its small movements smoothly and easily to accomplish the desired effect with the least amount of effort.

Test the truth of this statement by deliberately tensing all the muscles of the hand and arm. While maintaining this tension go through the movements of eating, picking a pin from the floor, brushing the hair. Observe the rigidity and jerkiness of these simple movements and the difficulty of regulating the energy expenditure required. As the appropriate muscles attempt to contract to move the hand, arm, or a finger, the contraction is resisted by the tension of the opposing muscles, and smooth action becomes impossible. Now allow the muscles to function normally in their relaxed state and repeat the same movements. This experiment illustrates in a slightly exaggerated form the difference between the movement and energy expenditure of the tense and the relaxed individual.

When muscle fiber is stimulated normally, it contracts, holds its shortened length until fatigue overcomes it, then relaxes to its original length during the recovery phase, while the fatigue products are either removed or converted again into potential energy supplies. The muscle fiber is strengthened by this experience of *contraction and recovery,* and it is again ready to receive a stimulus which will cause it to contract in a normal manner. But if a new stimulus reaches the fiber before the recovery process is complete, the fiber fails to relax completely and begins to contract from its slightly shortened length. Again it shortens as much as it is able to do, but because it was still fatigued at the beginning of the contraction, the second contraction is not so strong as the first, although the resulting fatigue is greater. If this process is repeated again and again by too frequent stimulation, the muscle fiber is weakened by being constantly fatigued without opportunity for full recovery, and its normal function is disturbed to such an extent that it cannot fully relax. It remains in a state of increased tonus, or tension, and its contractions are short, may be erratic, and are difficult to control.

When this state of tension is maintained over long periods of time, the individual becomes fatigued. With increasing fatigue his work becomes more and more inefficient. He works harder to produce the same results, which in turn produces greater fatigue. He becomes the victim of a vicious cycle of events which he is unable to control, and he becomes chronically tired and physically tense. He is suffering from *residual neuromuscular hypertension.* (*Residual* refers to the residue of fatigue, or the fatigue remaining or left over from each preceding muscle contraction; *neuromuscular* refers to the control of muscles by the motor-nerve stimuli; and *hypertension* means more tense, or greater tension than the normal amount.) He is no longer a physically efficient person because he is expending great amounts of energy which are producing no results other than fatigue. He is also a very tired person and his ability to enjoy life is reduced. He may show other physical symptoms such as indigestion, constipation, increased blood pressure, headaches, or a vague state of general physical discomfort. Tired as he is, he will find it difficult to sleep, and his sleep will not be restful. Unfortunately, a great many people today exist in this state of "chronic fatigue."

In the chronically tense individual the urge to activity finds no constructive outlet, but it may find outlets in actions which are in no way related to the problem which created the tension. His fingers may drum on the table aimlessly or forcibly to express irritation. He moves in his chair in an endless attempt to find a comfortable position. His hand reaches up to twist a lock of hair, or scratch the scalp, or pull at an ear. Walking becomes a sharp staccato of heels striking the floor. The pencil is gripped until the fingers become numb. The hand resting in the lap twists a handkerchief or clasps the other hand in a deathlike grip. The face twitches, the teeth are gritted, and the shoulders shrug. As the overstimulated individual sits "motionless," he twists a ring endlessly about his finger, he lights a cigarette and throws it away, he crosses and uncrosses his legs and wraps his feet about each other, and his mouth moves in meaningless grimaces. His physiological engine is racing, but the brakes are on; the car is still in low gear and the energy is being expended without serving any useful purpose. He complains of being tired, but he cannot stop these useless movements. The more tired he becomes, the more he worries, the more he is frustrated, the more easily he becomes angry, and the more his body mobilizes its forces for action in response to the stimuli set up by his mental state. But the normal action response to this stimulation is still more or less completely inhibited. The muscles remain in a state of constant tension, victims of the conflict between the normal response to the stimulus to act and the inhibition of that response in conformity with the demands of civilized living. Smooth, easy coordination of movement is lost, and fatigue is piled upon fatigue in the expenditure of unproductive effort without sufficient opportunity for recovery.

The fundamental approach to the reduction of tension lies in recognizing the underlying problems which are producing the worry, the fear, the anxiety, or the frustration. When a problem has been consciously recognized and analyzed, it can be dealt with. Either a solution can be found for it or no solution appears possible at the moment. If the solution can be found, then the problem and its resulting tensions may be dissipated in action. If no solution is possible, then the intelligent person recognizes the situation and attempts to find some way to live with the problem without allowing it to be a continual source of anxiety. A bit of Oriental philosophy expresses it this way:

For three things I pray:
The serenity to accept that which cannot be changed;
The courage to change that which can be changed;
And the wisdom to tell the one from the other.

This rational approach to the reduction of tension looks at the underlying causes. The physical approach helps to provide the temporary relief from physical tension which many people need to enable them to rest sufficiently to get a clearer mental picture of the problems which created the tension in the first place.

Physical activity may be used to divert the mind, to change the pattern of mental concentration, to give the mind a rest from thinking either consciously or subconsciously about a problem. This is relaxation through play, sports, games, or diversion. The golfer on the first tee may be tense, with part of his mind still on the problems of his personal life. But as he moves from hole to hole, his mind becomes more and more engrossed in the intricacies of this absorbing game, and he leaves his workaday worries behind him. His mind works on a new set of problems, but his mental pattern has changed temporarily from its previous worried state. As he swings, walks, bends over to pick up his clubs or remove the ball from the cup, his muscles contract and relax, and energy is spent in a normal pattern of full contraction of the muscle fiber followed by recovery. At the end of the game his body is normally fatigued, but he "feels good" because he has released the tensions created by his worried mind. He is mentally re-created. He can now approach his serious problems with a "rested" mind, which has broken its squirrel-in-a-cage pattern of worry and anxiety.

The tennis player must concentrate on his game and his opponent; the swimmer changes his environment; and even the bridge player finds mental diversion in giving his worried mind a new set of problems to cope with—small specific problems which permit of some solution in a reasonably short space of time. The habitual pattern of worry or fear or inadequacy is temporarily broken, and the physical tensions arising from those frustrations are released. This is the recreation approach to relaxation.

Can the same effect be obtained without resorting to the golf course, the tennis courts, or the bridge table? Is it possible to release the submaximal tensions created by everyday problems without interrupting the working day of the individual?

The living muscle is always in a state of activity. It can not, while it is alive, "do nothing." It must "do something." The tense muscle is doing something which produces undesirable results. To change that situation, it must be given an action pattern which will produce desirable results. Since the action pattern of the muscle is determined by the nerve impulses which originate in the brain, the problem is mental as well as physical, and the brain must consciously originate and direct the new action pattern.

The ability to relax at will is acquired in the same manner that any other neuromuscular skill is learned. It must first be experienced and the "feeling" of it perceived; then it must be practiced until the feeling can be reproduced whenever desired. The first step, then, is to acquire the *kinesthetic perception,* or the feeling, of relaxation. The second step is to practice until this feeling can be reproduced at will. The third step is to reproduce that feeling voluntarily in potentially tension-creating situations.

Begin the exploration of the relaxation process by lying on the floor, face up. In this energy-saving position, consciously tense every muscle in the body to increase awareness of the feeling of tension. Kinesthetic perception, or bodily awareness, of the feeling of tension must be developed, for many people are so habitually in the tense state that they do not recognize the feeling of tension when it exists. Such persons never learn to relax because they are not aware of the difference between the feeling of tension and the feeling of relaxation. Hold this state of extreme tension until the feeling becomes almost intolerable. Then release the tension, and stretch and twist and yawn and squirm and wiggle the body as a cat or a child does when it wakes from a long sleep.

The stretching process is not necessary for relaxation, but in the beginning stages it serves a useful purpose. It breaks the pattern of too rapid neuromuscular stimulation and sets up a new and opposing pattern of slow, sustained movement. It also improves the physiological state of the muscle by its effect on the capillaries. In the tense muscle the capillaries are slightly squeezed by the shortened, thickened muscle fibers, and the free passage of blood through the capillaries is interfered with. The exchange of oxygen and fatigue products is slowed down, and normal recovery does not take place. Alternately contracting the muscle fibers and pulling them to their normal length by stretching, twisting, and squirming tends to release the pressure on the capillaries, and the circulation within the muscle is improved as the capillaries are released. The blood pressure is lowered and the heart rate slows as the resistance to the passage of blood through the arteries and capillaries is decreased.

For many persons, the greatest tension will be found in the muscles of the upper back and the back of the neck. More forcible stretching may be needed for these areas. Lying on the back, clasp the hands behind the bulge of the back of the head. Keeping the shoulders on the ground, pull forward with the arms to raise the head from the mat. Use a "bounce pull." Pull strongly, then "give" slightly, pull a little harder, then "give" again, until a strong stretch is felt in the extensor muscles of the neck.

Then localize the pull farther down across the shoulders. Still lying on the back, clasp the hands in front of the body between the legs. Pull forward with the hands and arms to raise the head and shoulders from the mat. Again use the bounce pull, of pull and release, pull a little harder, release, and continue until a strong stretch is felt in the muscles of the upper spine and across the shoulders.

Still lying on the floor, with the arms at the sides, bend the knees and place the feet on the floor as close to the buttocks as possible. Using strong abdominal muscle contraction, rotate the pelvic girdle so the *coccyx* (tail bone) moves forward and upward. Slowly continue the movement, raising the hips from the floor, and slowly continue the lift until the back is entirely off the floor and the weight is borne by the legs and shoulders (Fig. 6). Rest in this position before beginning the descent. Let the back curve, and try to get the feeling of hanging in a hammock supported from the knees and the shoulders. Again contract the abdominal muscles strongly, "pick up the tuck," and

Fig. 6. The weight is borne by the legs and shoulders as the trunk hangs like a hammock from the two points of support.

slowly return to the back-lying position. This should be a smooth continuous movement with no sudden stops and starts, and the feeling should be one of coming up from the floor vertebra by vertebra and returning vertebra by vertebra in the reverse order. Counting will help keep the movement slow and smooth. Begin by going from the back-lying position to the hanging position to a slow count of ten; rest for a count of five, then return to the lying position to a slow count of ten, letting the legs slide slowly down to their extended position as soon as the hips are on the floor. As control is acquired, increase the count to twenty, to thirty, or even to forty.

This slow controlled use of the abdominal muscles requires concentration, which makes it impossible for the mind to think of anything else while the exercise is in progress. The muscles of the back are gently stretched by gravity while in the hanging position. Breathing becomes slower and deeper, the heart beats more slowly, and the entire body feels rested and less restless. Lie quietly on the floor and enjoy the feeling of inactivity and the lack of desire for activity for a short space of time.

The legs and arms may feel a bit cramped from being so long in a held position. Give them the same slow-movement treatment. Begin with the legs extended, with the heels and ankle bones touching. Again using the slow count, smoothly rotate the legs on their long axis until the little toes are touching the floor. Get this rotation all the way from the hip joint as the legs slowly turn away from each other. Hold this stretched position briefly, then reverse the rotation to bring the legs back together again.

Start with the arms at the sides, palms down. To a slow count of ten, turn the hand and arm over until the palm is face up and the back of the hand is resting on the floor. Again, get the rotation from the shoulder joint as well as from the elbow and wrist joints. Hold the stretched position briefly, then return the arms and hands to their starting position to another slow count of ten.

If the body feels uncomfortable at any point, or the arms or legs feel uncomfortable as they return to the starting position, move the part *very slowly* to a more comfortable position and allow it to come to rest. Do not jerk or twitch the body to a new position; just move it slowly, and enjoy the sensation of relaxed movement.

Even when the muscles of the body are relaxed, the head and face may still show signs of tension. Slowly turn the head from side to side, using ten counts to turn it to the left and another ten counts to turn it forward again; then turn it right and forward, and allow it to come to rest in a comfortable position. For many people this comfortable position is with the head turned to one side rather than straight forward.

Tension in the muscles of the face is so habitual that it is difficult to recognize. Intensify the tension of the facial muscles by gritting the teeth, closing the eyes tightly, and in general making the face as short as possible. Reverse the muscle pulls by making the face as long as possible, stretching the mouth wide and opening the eyes as far as they will go. Give the facial muscles a little exercise by alternating the short face with the long face, making the changes slowly but definitely. Then starting from the long position, very slowly allow the facial muscles to relax as the eyes close, the mouth closes, and the face resumes its normal length. Do this easily, slowly, and resist the temptation to let the teeth snap together and to set the jaw. The teeth should not quite touch each other as the lips close lightly.

The eyes may still need some individual treatment, for these very active muscles find it difficult to relax. Open the eyes wide, then shut them tightly. Open, shut, then from the open position let the lids come down as slowly as possible, gently closing the eyes and stopping just as the light is shut out. As the internal muscles of the eye begin to relax, the eyeballs seem to drop farther and farther back into the head, and the eyes no longer "see" mental images.

Now move the body slowly into its most comfortable position. Move the feet and legs slowly to relieve any last vestiges of tension from the held position; open the hands slowly and let them close partially in the curved flexed position; move the head slowly to find the most comfortable spot for it; or slowly roll the entire body over to the face-lying position, if that is more comfortable. Then just lie there. Sleep may come or it may not come, depending upon the need of the body for sleep at that moment, but the body and the mind are at rest.

When the rest period is over, return slowly to the state of normal activity. Open the eyes slowly; roll the head around slowly; yawn, stretch, and easily come to a sitting position. Stretch again, then without haste get to a standing position and move quietly on to the next task, refreshed by this brief period of release from tension.

During the learning process, one of the objectives is to

develop kinesthetic perception of the difference between the relaxed and the tense states. Try this experiment: After reaching as great a degree of relaxation as possible, suddenly sit up with a start with every muscle tense. The telephone rings, a car backfires outside the window, or the belated remembrance of an appointment not kept galvanizes the body into sudden action. Every muscle is tense, the heart beats faster, breathing becomes rapid and shallow, and the mind darts frantically about trying to think of a dozen things at the same time. Identify the feeling of tension, then try to release it by returning to the former blissful state of relaxation. Tense, relax, tense, relax. Practice controlling the body responses voluntarily and at will. Be as relaxed as possible, then be as tense as possible—and recognize that the mind can control the reactions of the body. No one needs to be continually tense unless he wishes to be tense or has no desire to relax.

This extended flat-on-the-back approach to relaxation should be used to develop the perception of what physical relaxation means. It is also useful for getting maximum refreshment out of short rest periods, or for inducing sleep when an unusual degree of tension makes sleep elusive. For practical purposes in daily living, however, the ability to relax must be developed without going through all the preliminary exercises and stretches.

Practice the next step in a situation where only the mind is occupied and the body needs to do nothing but sit quietly while the mind follows the movie, the lecture, or the radio program. Using the recently developed kinesthetic perception of tension, note the position of the shoulders. Are they stiff, hunched, or held back? Move them slowly and easily and let them drop to their normal, balanced position. Are the legs held stiffly or the feet twisted around each other? Move them slowly and let them find a position of comfort without strain. Are the hands twiddling with a pencil, clasping each other, holding stiffly on to the arm of the chair? Slowly stretch them and allow them to rest quietly and easily in a softly curled position. Is the neck tense with the strain of holding the head forward to look or listen? Stretch the muscles in the back of the neck by dropping the head forward, then let the head come back to a position of rest and support on the neck. Check the entire body to see where energy is being spent by needless tension or strained positions. Move slowly into a comfortable position and recapture the feeling of relaxation developed when lying on the floor. Let the mind work while the body rests.

It may be necessary to repeat this checking process a number of times at first, for the habit of tension is strong, and the body tends to return to its habitual tensed state. This practice, however, gradually increases the kinesthetic perception of tension, and the need to consciously check the position of the body parts becomes less and less frequent as the less conscious part of the brain takes over the responsibility.

When the ability to relax the body while only the mind is occupied has been mastered, the next step is to utilize that ability while the body is also engaged in some mild physical activity such as sitting at a table eating, writing, or typing. Before beginning the activity, check the feeling of tension in the legs and feet, the back, the shoulders, and the neck. If necessary, tense them as much as possible to intensify the kinesthetic perception of the feeling to be avoided. Then stretch gently and consciously release the tension in the parts of the body not actually engaged in the activity at hand. Do not jerk the body parts out of their held positions, but move them slowly and easily to the position of greatest relaxation and rest. Check at intervals to determine whether the feeling of tension has returned, then release it consciously before continuing to work with the hands. If this process is repeated frequently enough, it will become habitual, and the discomfort of the tense, held positions will serve as the stimulus to relaxation.

Driving a car offers a good test of the ability to relax the nonactive parts of the body while the mind is alert and the hands and feet must respond to what the eyes see and the ears hear. Tension usually centers in the shoulders and upper back, and it may be found also in the legs, which may be held stiffly in their respective positions behind the clutch and the accelerator. While driving, sit back against the cushion and let the shoulders drop to their normal resting level. Stretch the extensor muscles of the neck by bringing the head forward, then let the head return to its balanced position easily and without strain. Tense the muscles of the legs and feet, and let the tension go out of them. Contract the abdominal muscles to force the lower back against the seat, then let them relax easily, maintaining only enough tension to hold the body back against the cushions of the car.

Try these progressive tests for relaxation in car driving. First master the art of relaxing while driving. Then try to relax while someone else is driving. Recognize that nothing the passenger does can change the course of the car as the driver pilots it through traffic. Stop trying to mentally drive the car, slowing it down, speeding it up, putting on the brakes. The driver is in complete control of the situation, and the passenger might better relax and arrive at his destination rested and refreshed than remain tense and irritable with the frustration of trying to influence a situation over which he has no control. The final test, however, is to relax the body and mind when your own car is being driven by someone else! When this point has been reached, the technique of conscious relaxation while sitting has been mastered!

The next step in becoming a relaxed person is to learn to relax while walking or working in the standing position. Relaxation while moving may sound like a contradiction in terms, but actually it is not. It simply means using only those muscles required to perform the act, using them as economically as possible, and not using the other muscles to perform movements which do not contribute to the act or which interfere with it.

Observe the staccato walk of the tense person. The heels strike the pavement as if to drive a hole in it. The knees are locked by the tension of the opposing muscles at the knee joint. The legs move stiffly from the hip joint as tension in the extensors interferes with the easy action of the flexors as the leg is swung forward, and in turn the tense flexors resist the easy action of the extensors as the weight is transferred to the leading foot. This opposition of pulls rotates the pelvic girdle, and the lower back is hollowed as the buttocks protrude. The hips are jolted from side to side as the heels strike the pavement and the weight is pushed from side to side. The shoulders are held stiffly and may be slightly elevated. The upper arms are held close to the body by the strained position of the shoulder girdle, and the lower arms swing stiffly and awkwardly. The head pushes forward from the stiff shoulder girdle, or is held back by the tension of the extensor muscles of the neck. The smooth transfer of weight from foot to foot, the easy alternating swing and push of the legs, the rhythmic oscillation of the hips and the compensating shoulder swing are all hindered, distorted, and made awkward by the constant tension in the opposing muscles which resist the contraction of the active muscles.

Again try the experiment of consciously tensing every muscle in the body. Grit the teeth and frown to complete the picture. Hold this feeling of tension and walk rapidly about the room. Note the feeling of restraint, of interference with movement. Try to walk faster and observe how the heels strike the floor with a jar and the feeling of interference becomes almost unbearable. The tense walker may appear very energetic, and he is. He spends energy prodigally to accomplish the very simple task of moving his body from one place to another. He arrives physically and mentally breathless and vents his irritation on the first person he meets. He raps on the counter while waiting to be served; he slams the door as he enters the room because he is unable to control the force of his push on the door.

Do not stop walking, but consciously release the tension in the shoulders, the arms, the back, and the legs. Note the feeling of freedom of movement as contrasted with the previous restraint. Let the face relax from a frown to a smile, and observe the feeling of relief which follows. Continue walking, slowly, rapidly, languidly, or briskly. Alternate extreme tension with conscious relaxation, until the kinesthetic perception of both is well established. Practice this alternation of tension with relaxation while walking to school, while walking down the corridor, when starting out the door. Gradually the awareness of tension will become habitual to such an extent that the discomfort of the tense attitude will serve as an almost automatic stimulus to seek relief from it in relaxation.

Few people in this harried modern world ever achieve complete and constant relaxation without constant effort, for the frustrations which cause tension are persistent and ever-present. But the awareness of the physical sensation of tension can be developed to provide a reminder that the mind and body need "the pause that refreshes" by breaking the tense thought and action pattern which has been built. The rapid, jerky, unsynchronized pattern of thought and action can be slowed down, smoothed, and synchronized to bring into play only those ideas and muscles which act constructively in solving the problem.

Does this mean that the relaxed person always thinks and moves slowly? Far from it. It means that he expends mental and physical energy constructively, conserving it when it does not contribute to the solution of the problem and spending it freely when it does. The top-flight tennis athlete exemplifies this idea perfectly. Poised, relaxed, and at ease but mentally alert, he waits in a position of readiness until he sees where the ball is going. Then he moves quickly and exactly to that spot, holding his racket ready, and at exactly the right split second he swings the racket with a beautiful synchronized action directing all his energy into hitting the ball, driving it exactly where he wants it to go.

Contrast this with the tense beginner. He dances about on his toes, moving forward, backward, to the right, to the left. The ball moves toward him and he darts toward it, moving so rapidly that he must stop suddenly, throwing himself off balance so that the swing of his racket is not synchronized with the movement of his body, and the force is wasted in hitting too soon or too late. The ball bobbles forward to fall an easy prey to the skill of his opponent. The beginner is spending energy, but much of it is wasted because it is not directed toward accomplishment of the objective of hitting the ball in the direction in which he wants it to go. He loses much of the enjoyment of the game because so many of his movements are pointless and he has so little control over them.

The athlete speaks of "form" and "timing." These are also essential for successful daily living. They characterize every movement of the relaxed individual. The useless and obstructive motions are eliminated. The body moves easily in the performance of its tasks, unhindered by the restrictions of the tense opposing muscles. The rested and refreshed muscles perform their tasks with less fatigue, and that "tired feeling" vanishes into the limbo of useless things, as all energy expenditure is directed toward the accomplishment of the work to be done.

Relaxation is a physical state, but it is controlled by the mental state. It is acquired by the conscious effort to control the thought as well as the action pattern. It takes perception, practice, and willingness to train the mind into new habits of thinking and the body into new habits of action. Complete, habitual relaxation with no unnecessary tension is probably not achievable for most individuals, but the ability to voluntarily relax the body even occasionally is an accomplishment well worth the time, effort, and practice it takes.

The practical use of this ability in the situations of everyday living depends on two things: the awareness of tension, which comes first, then the willingness and ability to redirect the mental and physical reaction pattern to replace tension with normal relaxation.

Take a commonplace incident like missing a streetcar. The first reaction is one of irritation. Tension develops, and the would-be rider stands impatiently on the curb, looking at his watch, worrying about how late he will be for the appointment, twisting and fidgeting—but the next streetcar comes no sooner. The relaxed individual recognizes the tension arising from his irritation and also recognizes that all his fidgeting, grimacing, and foot tapping uses energy while contributing nothing to the solution of the problem. He consciously stops the fidgeting by moving his body slowly and easily over to the bench, sits down quietly, and spends the five minutes at his disposal for relaxed rest. He turns his mind to interested observation of the passers-by or to constructive thinking on some matter of interest to him. When the streetcar does come, he climbs on it, finds the most comfortable spot available, either standing or sitting, and again recognizes that here is a situation in which he can relax and rest. The same technique is useful in any standing-in-line situation. If he must wait, then wait he must, and no amount of energy used in grimacing, irritated weight shifting, or grumbling will shorten the wait one minute. The waiting is inevitable; the tension developed or the relaxation achieved is entirely up to the waiter.

Any irritating situation will serve for another example. An error is found in a report, a school grade seems unfair, or someone else has done something which causes inconvenience and annoyance. The tense person grits his teeth, sets his jaw, and rises from his chair full of determination to bring the offender to an accounting. He starts out in haste, his heels pounding, his shoulders held stiffly, every line in his body showing the tension resulting from his irritation. He reaches his destination and vents his wrath on the culprit—only to find that he has been misinformed or has misinterpreted the information. The culprit responds with indignation, and a full-fledged crisis is in the making. The relaxed person avoids all this. As his first irritation expresses itself, he recognizes the feeling of tension. He consciously slows his movements and relaxes his muscles. As he does so, his mind attacks the problem more rationally and he sets out in an easy, purposeful manner, not to vent his wrath, but to ascertain the facts in the case. The tense person wasted his energy and made himself ridiculous; the relaxed person used his physical and mental energy purposefully to discover a solution to the problem.

Or watch two people eating in the cafeteria. Both have just fifteen minutes to go down the line, pick up their food, eat it, and return to work. The tense individual finds the line ahead of him. While he waits impatiently, he works himself into a high state of tension. As his turn comes he slams the food on his tray, goes to his table and jerks out a chair, and then begins to gobble his food as rapidly as he can, watching the clock all the while. In the afternoon, he takes bicarbonate of soda for his indigestion. The relaxed person is also in a hurry and irritated by the delay. But he senses the tension of his irritation and consciously relaxes his body as he waits his turn. He reaches his table, and again he recognizes the tense impulse to shovel his food down as rapidly as he can. But he also knows he will finish just as soon and in far better condition if he easily and purposefully cuts up his food, transfers it to his mouth, and chews it before swallowing it. So he consciously relaxes his muscles and enjoys the pleasant function of eating.

The list might be multiplied endlessly. Planned reminders that it is "time to relax" can be included in the day's work. The relaxation-conscious desk worker places his telephone far enough from his chair so that he must stretch to reach it. The stretch relieves the strain of the held position and provides a prelude to conscious release of the tension accumulated by the concentration on mental work. He relaxes as he brings the telephone to him and slowly and easily raises the receiver from the hook. The worker who sits all day uses the completion of a given task as a signal for relaxation. He deliberately stretches his neck muscles by bringing his head forward, humps his shoulders, and strongly contracts his abdominal muscles to push his lower back firmly erect against the back of the chair. The standing worker finds opportunities to move about and sets signals, such as the handing of change to a customer or the ringing up of a sale on the cash register, to remind him to consciously relax the tension in his back, his knees, and his shoulders. Each person can devise his own "time to relax" signals out of the events of his working day. In time the response to these signals will become habitual. These deliberate relaxations of tension bring restful changes of tempo, both mental and physical. This reduces the day's fatigue, which results not only from the day's work but also from the tension developed in response to the emotional stimuli of that work.

To sum up briefly, the essence of relaxation is, needless tension wastes energy. The tense person runs when walking would get him there more economically; he paces the floor when he might stand still; he jumps up or fidgets in his chair when he might rest by sitting quietly; and he lies awake uncomfortably when he might go to sleep. He is always putting forth maximum effort and getting minimum results because his energy is not directed toward the accomplishment of his objectives; he actually works too hard and accomplishes too little.

The relaxed person is one who does not waste his energy. He never runs when walking will get him there on time; he never paces the floor when he might stand at ease; he never fidgets in his chair when he might sit quietly; and when he lies down, he goes to sleep. But whether he lies, sits, stands, walks, runs, or works, he does so purposefully and easily; he makes every motion count; and he accomplishes maximum results with a minimum expenditure of energy.

This discussion would not be complete without a comment

on the relationship of relaxation to sleep. The tense individual usually complains of insomnia. He retires but finds himself unable to go to sleep. His mind continues to race futilely over the problems of the day; and when he has nothing else to worry about he worries about the inability to sleep with a long day coming. The tense individual needs to prepare for sleep before going to bed. He needs to break his mental and physical action pattern and relax both his mind and his body before he reaches his bed. Many techniques can be used, but any slow-moving activity different from the activities of the day or evening will serve the purpose.

Sit down in a comfortable chair, well supported. Consciously relax the muscles of the arms, the legs, the back, noting any tendencies to grip the chair arms, twiddle with the upholstery, or wrap the legs around each other. Sit as restfully as possible, making all movements slow, controlled, and purposeful. Pick up a popular magazine with lightweight reading content. Read a story or an article—anything to divert the mind from its daily problems and break the worry pattern of thinking. Some people like a cool or a warm drink while reading. Others do not need to read but may just sit and listen to the radio. Others may find it satisfying to just sit. The point of the sitting is to slow the physical reactions of the body while consciously diverting the mind.

Move slowly to the bedroom, and perform the usual going-to-bed routines with slow, controlled easy motions. Wind the alarm clock and set it for morning without irritation. Why be irritated? Everyone has to get up in the morning, and no amount of irritation at night will alter by one minute the necessity for arising in time to get to work or to school at the stated hour. Get slowly into bed, stretch luxuriously, and enjoy the comfortable feeling of lying supported on a soft surface. Resist any temptation to let the mind take just one more review of the problems and irritations of today or tomorrow. Concentrate on the feeling of comfort and the realization that for the next eight hours no problems need be solved. If the prebed routine has been really slow and relaxing, there will be no need to recall the rest of this paragraph. Either sleep will come, or it will make no difference whether it comes or not.

But the habit of tension is stubborn. The remembered irritations crop up; the muscles tense; the body jerks about in bed, tossing from side to side in response to the irritating stimuli. Direct measures may be necessary. Use the routine described earlier for bringing about almost complete relaxation in the lying position. Stretch, then use the hands to pull the shoulders forward, then pull the head forward. Slowly raise the body to the bridge position, counting to keep the movement slow, smooth, and controlled. Slowly lower the body and allow the legs and feet to slide down. If the bridge position is too difficult on a springy bed, slow abdominal contraction may be used instead. Lying flat on the back with the knees extended, slowly contract the abdominal muscles to a count of ten, rotating the pelvic girdle and flattening the lower back. Hold the full contraction for ten more counts, then slowly release the contraction to another count of ten. Then slowly rotate the legs and arms, counting to make the mind concentrate on the movement. If this is done thoroughly and conscientiously, the mind cannot think about anything else. If the mind tends to wander back to its all-engrossing problems, sternly bring it back to the immediate problem of producing slow controlled movement. Stretch the face and let the muscles relax. Open the eyes wide and close them easily. Get the feeling of the eyeballs moving farther and farther back into the head as the muscles of the eyes relax. Then move slowly to a comfortable position and lie there completely relaxed. If a leg or arm is uncomfortable and still feels the need of movement, move it slowly and easily to a new position. Do not jerk or twitch the body. Make all movements slow and controlled. If sleep fails to come immediately, do not worry about it. Sleep is not important if the body is at rest.

Relaxed sleep refreshes the body, and relaxed waking preserves the feeling of refreshment. No two people are quite alike in their response to waking up in the morning. Some spring from their beds full of energy to greet the new day; others "come alive" slowly and need time to make the physical transition from the state of rest to the state of activity. The slow waker needs to take his time in getting up when the alarm clock sounds, even though he may have to set it five minutes earlier to give himself time to wake up. He needs to stretch, yawn, and stretch some more to get his muscles ready for their more strenuous tasks. As he stretches, he contracts his abdominal muscles to increase the return of blood to the heart to increase the circulation to his inactive brain. He blinks his eyes and stretches his face to get his muscles ready to smile, as he rises to begin a new day without irritation or physical tension.

No one can escape the irritations, annoyances, and worries of life. It is entirely normal for the body to respond to these irritations by increased tension. The secret of relaxed and efficient living is to recognize these tensions when they occur, then consciously change the mental and physical pattern of reaction to redirect the body into purposeful activity. This can be done by consciously substituting smooth, easy action for tense, jerky action, thus releasing the feeling of tension so that the mind can take a new look at its problems and treat them rationally and effectively instead of emotionally and ineffectively. This is the physical approach to a mental problem which expresses itself physically through body action.

PROJECTS FOR FURTHER STUDY

1. Make a list of all the things which seem to irritate you in one day. Which ones could you do something about? Which ones were unavoidable? What did you accomplish in each instance by being irritated?

2. For just one day decide that you will not be irritated by anything that happens. Whenever an irritating situation occurs, consciously relax your muscles. Keep the "box score" on your successes and failures. At the end of the day honestly answer the question, "Was it worth doing?"

3. If you drive a car, count the number of stop lights and stop streets between your home and school or place of business. At each intersection note the number of drivers who are showing annoyance or irritation. Aren't they ridiculous? For one week deliberately practice relaxation each time you come to a stop light. Doesn't it make you feel adult and superior?

4. If you ride on the streetcar or bus every day, study the people who are riding with you. How many of them are wasting energy? Are you? For one week consciously plan to use the streetcar or bus as a "place to relax." Did it take you any longer to get to your destination?

CHAPTER

5

Exercise and Abdominal Function

THE TONE and elasticity of the abdominal muscles affect the functioning of many body systems. Digestion, elimination, circulation, and menstruation may be influenced adversely by a stretched and flaccid abdominal wall. Exercises which strengthen and improve the control of the abdominal muscles may be far-reaching in their desirable effects.

Poor digestion accompanied by constipation is one of the commonest complaints of civilized man and woman. Sedentary living, lack of exercise, highly refined diets, and tension all contribute to this interference with normal elimination. Exercise is not a panacea, but properly used it may contribute to the relief of some types of nonpathological constipation.

Peristalsis, the process of moving the food materials along the intestinal tract (see Chapter 2), is interfered with if the intestines are allowed to sag downward and forward. The weight of the waste mass must be moved upward against the downward pull of gravity, and this requires stronger peristaltic contractions. The walls of the intestines are stretched more and more and gradually lose their elasticity. The waste mass accumulates in the intestinal tract, or moves forward sluggishly, and constipation results.

Laxatives and lubricants may temporarily relieve this condition, but they will not prevent its recurrence, since they do

77

nothing to correct the cause. These "relief" agents may act in one of several ways. Some act by irritating the lining of the intestinal tract, causing it to contract convulsively to expel the waste mass. Others contain sufficient salt to cause the intestine to absorb large amounts of water. The waste mass is diluted to make it more fluid, and the additional volume created by the added fluid stretches the intestine sufficiently to cause strong peristaltic contractions. Still others act as lubricating agents by mixing oils with the waste material to make it move along more readily.

Exercise may be used to relieve constipation by creating pressure with churning and massaging movements which squeeze the swollen large intestine and mechanically force the waste materials toward the lower bowel. Exercise may also be used to correct some of the causes of constipation and prevent its recurrence. It must be emphasized, however, that persistent constipation may be a medical problem arising from one of many causes. The consistently constipated individual should consult a physician to determine the specific cause and follow the procedures recommended for treatment.

Specific twisting and churning action may be induced by Exercise Nos. 19 and 21 to 25. Direct pressure may be applied to the abdominal contents by Nos. 12, 13*b*, 18, and 20. Any general activity which uses the large muscles of the trunk, increases the body metabolism, and "stirs up" the sluggish circulation also will be helpful. Numbers 23, 31, and 32 might be used for this purpose.

More important than immediate relief, however, is prevention of constipation by improving the tone and control of the abdominal wall by consistent exercise of this vital area. Numbers 9, 10, and 13*b* used daily will strengthen the abdominal wall so that it can provide the resistance needed to hold the abdominal contents firmly in place.

Constipation also may result from tension, worry, or emotional disturbances. Relaxation techniques described in Chapter 4 may prove helpful in such cases.

The efficiency of the circulatory system is also affected by the tone of the abdominal muscles. As the blood returns to the heart from all parts of the body, it is collected into the large veins which pass through the abdomen. These veins may contain at one time as much as one-third of the total volume of blood in the body. This blood is moved on to the heart by the pumping action of the diaphragm (see Chapter 2). If the abdominal muscles are stretched and flabby, they are unable to resist the pressure applied by the downward thrust of the diaphragm. The abdominal wall moves forward and "gives" with the downward movement of the diaphragm, and little pressure is produced to move the blood in the large veins on to the veins in the thoracic cavity and into the heart. The heart cannot send out blood it does not receive, and the body is forced to work on half rations. The brain receives an insufficient amount of aerated blood, and the individual complains of being dizzy and lightheaded. He cannot concentrate or think clearly with his oxygen-hungry brain.

This effect is felt most keenly in the morning after a night spent in the horizontal position. The body has been relatively quiet, and much blood has pooled in the abdominal veins. As the sleeper rises to an erect position, the abdominal wall sags forward and the blood remains in the abdominal veins instead of being pushed on to the heart. Such a person is sometimes heard to complain, "I can't do a thing in the morning until I get my girdle on." An elastic girdle is needed to hold the abdominal wall in place only when the muscular "four-way stretch girdle" is in poor condition.

Exercises needed to improve the venous return of blood to the heart should include activity for all sets of abdominal muscles, crosswise and diagonal as well as vertical. Numbers 9, 10, 11, 12, 17, 18, and 23 will produce this result if used consistently.

Difficult or painful menstruation (*dysmenorrhea*) is probably the greatest single cause of loss of woman power and of feminine inefficiency in the civilized world. Most of it is needless, and much of it is psychological rather than physiological. Girls have been taught to regard their menstrual period as a "sick time" or "the curse" of womanhood. They are taught to coddle themselves, to expect to be miserable, and to rush for the aspirin, the hot-water bottle, and the bed at the slightest sign of discomfort. Expecting to be miserable, they find it easy to magnify every slight pain into an unbearable cramp, and by being inactive they increase whatever symptoms they may have. This is an old-fashioned approach to menstruation, as out of place in this modern age of activity as the surrey with the fringe on top.

Menstruation is a normal function, and for the healthy girl or woman should be no more inconvenient than digestion or elimination. The occurrence of menstruation is only one point in a constantly changing rhythmic physiologic cycle which is controlled and regulated by the secretions of the endocrine glands. If the delicately balanced mechanism is upset in any way, pain and distress may result, but normally the balance is maintained without interference by the individual. The biochemical changes that occur preceding and during menstruation may produce a state of heightened irritability, in which the threshold to pain is lower than at other times. This is another way of saying that discomfort is more readily perceived at this time, and pain which might be ignored at other times becomes magnified.

At the beginning of the menstrual period, when most cramps occur, the abdominal cavity is more congested than usual by the presence of an additional quantity of blood. This produces increased pressure on the sensory nerves, and the sensation of pain may be experienced. If the congestion is increased by constipation, or by allowing the abdominal contents to sag forward and downward against a slack abdominal wall, the pressure on the sensory nerves will also be increased and the pain may become acute. Fatigue, worry, or emotional tension also may affect the sensitivity of the pain nerves and increase the sensation of discomfort.

Two problems exist: the first is to relieve the discomfort if it exists; the second is to prevent the discomfort from recurring at the next menstrual period. Appropriate exercise may be used in the solution of both problems.

To relieve the pain, it is necessary to relieve the congestion. Cruel though it may sound, activity which increases the rate of circulation and requires strong contractions of the abdominal muscles is the quickest way to relieve the pain. Walking up four flights of stairs or climbing a long hill is very helpful. If this seems impossible to do, a milder approach is to invert the body, placing it in a position in which the hips are higher than the head. The direct approach is to lie with the legs on the bed while the head rests on a pillow on the floor. A milder method is to lie in bed with the pillow under the hips instead of under the head. If night cramps are anticipated, they may often be prevented by this simple procedure.

The hot-water bottle may be used as a form of artificial exercise. The heat increases circulation in the area to which it is applied and in addition tends to dull the sensitivity of the pain nerves, decreasing the awareness of pain until the congestion is relieved.

The prevention of pain is far more important than temporary relief after it occurs. The most useful exercise for this purpose was devised by Dr. Harvey E. Billig, Jr. It was designed to stretch the fascial-ligamentous bands through which the sensory nerves pass. (Fascia are the thin membranes which cover the muscles and muscle fibers. At the ends of the muscle the fascia converge into thick bands, or ligaments, for attachment to the bone.) By such stretching, the pressure on the nerves is lessened and the sensation of pain is reduced. This exercise, popularly known as the Billig Stretch, is described in the Appendix, No. 46.

There are some cases of dysmenorrhea which arise from malformation, endocrine imbalance, or poor health and which cannot be relieved by exercise. Fortunately these are in the minority, but any case of severe dysmenorrhea which does not respond to exercise should be referred to a physician for diagnosis and treatment. Where no pathological cause exists, exercise will help in the vast majority of cases. At least it is worth a try!

It may be of interest to note that the Billig Stretch exercise is used by many track and field athletes to increase the mobility of the hip joint. Sprinters, distance runners, hurdlers, and jumpers find it particularly helpful.

PROJECTS FOR FURTHER STUDY

1. Stand before a full-length mirror. Let your shoulders slump and your abdomen protrude as much as possible. Hold the position for three minutes, then straighten up to your normal standing position. Why did you sigh?
2. In the same position with abdomen protruding, try to take a deep breath. Why is it difficult? Straighten up, assuming a balanced position with the abdominal wall flat. Again try to take a deep breath. Why is it easier?
3. Practice Exercise No. 46 until you understand exactly how to do it. Beginning on the day after your menstrual period ends, do it every day for one month. Compare your feeling during the next menstrual period with the way you usually feel at that time.
4. Teach Exercise No. 46 to someone else. Explain the theory of the exercise and its general purpose.
5. For one week count the number of advertisements for laxatives that you see in the newspaper and on television and hear on the radio. On the basis of your findings, comment on the statement, "Constipation is the universal affliction of modern civilization."

CHAPTER

6

Exercise and Weight Control

ONE OF THE most persistent quests of mankind—and woman-kind—is for a simple effortless method of decreasing body weight. Diet, drugs, massage, electrical stimulation, and exercise all have their advocates among those who would be completely happy if they could only lose ten pounds. Diet requires self-denial; drugs are dangerous unless taken under medical supervision, and massage and passive exercise are expensive. Consequently, for most people the quest narrows down to a search for an easy exercise which may be done in not more than five minutes a day and which will melt the unwanted pounds away—but only "in the right places." Unfortunately, there is only one exercise which really is effective: *shake the head slowly from side to side when offered a second helping.* And even this one is not guaranteed to "take it off in the right places."

Body weight depends on many factors. The size and weight of the bones, the amount and quality of the musculature, the weight of the viscera, the weight of blood in the veins and arteries, and the fatty deposits throughout the body all are included in the number of pounds which the scales register. Of these many variables, the amount and quality of fat deposited in the body is the most subject to change for any individual. Where such fatty deposits are present, it is possible to "reduce" them; body weight or build resulting from any of the other factors is either difficult or impossible to alter.

Food is taken into the body by eating. The digestive system converts the energy components of the food into blood sugar. The remainder of the food passes through the intestinal tract and is eliminated. The blood sugar is used as a fuel by the muscles and is burned as needed to supply the energy for muscle contraction. If the supply of blood sugar is in excess of the amount being burned by the muscles, that which cannot be stored in the liver is converted into fat and stored for future use in depositories at various points throughout the body. Whenever the needs of the muscles are in excess of the sugar supplied by the current intake of food, the deposited fat is again reconverted into fuel and this fuel is burned to provide the muscles with energy. Simply stated: if the intake of food is greater than the output of energy, fat is deposited and body weight increases; if the output of energy is greater than the intake of food, fat is burned as fuel and body weight decreases.

The endocrine glands, particularly the thyroid and the pituitary, have much to do with the rate at which the body burns its fuel (*basal metabolism*). Some people are like twelve-cylinder cars; they get very low mileage from their fuel and burn it at an extravagant rate. They "eat and eat and never get fat." Other people have more economical physiological engines, like the bantam cars that get forty miles to the gallon. They complain that they "eat scarcely enough to keep a bird alive," but still they gain weight. These are factors which vary with the individual, but the basic principle applies to everyone: if you eat more food than your body burns, you will gain weight; if your body consumes more food fuel than you eat, you will lose weight.

It is obvious, then, that there are two approaches to weight control: decrease the intake, or increase the output. The first method, difficult though it is for those who enjoy eating, is the easier method. The second method, which sounds easier, is extremely difficult and requires an expenditure of energy greater than the average individual is willing to make.

Unusual, elaborate, bizarre, or starvation diets should not be undertaken except on the advice of a physician. Any diet which promises to decrease the body weight by more than one or two pounds a week is dangerous unless it is supervised by a physician who is able to watch the patient carefully and note any signs of damage to the physiological economy of the body. Fat may be destroyed by such a diet, but also it is quite possible to destroy the proteins of the body in extreme dieting, and it is relatively easy to upset the whole digestive process to such an extent that the body loses its ability to assimilate food and maintain itself in a healthy state.

The body functions best on a balanced diet which includes fats and carbohydrates as well as proteins and low-energy bulky foods. The complete omission of any group of foodstuffs from the diet for an extended period of time is dangerous to the health of the individual, and the results may be far-reaching and long-lasting. The only sensible "diet" is to decrease the total *amount* of food eaten each day while maintaining the same proportionate balance among the various food groups. This may be a slower process than any of the starvation diets, but it is much safer. One or two pounds a week may be lost on such a program, and that is about as much as the normal, active individual can lose without discomfort or danger.

Daily weighings serve as an index to the success of such a plan. If the weight continues to increase, the intake is still exceeding the output; if the weight remains stationary, a balance between intake and output has been reached, and the intake must be decreased further. But if day by day the scales register a few ounces less, then the intake has been reduced to less than the output and body fat is being consumed. It must be emphasized again, however, that any extensive program of weight reduction involving a loss of more than ten pounds should *never* be undertaken without the advice and supervision of a physician.

Why go without food? Why not eat all you like and then "exercise it away?" This sounds easy, but it is really very difficult because great amounts of exercise are needed to burn away even a small amount of stored fat. Physiologists have computed the amounts of *additional* exercise needed to burn away one pound of stored fat. A few examples will serve to convince the most doubtful. For the average individual to burn one pound of stored fat, it would be necessary for him to walk to the top of the Washington monument 48 times, walk briskly on level ground for 19½ hours, ride horseback at a walk for 44 hours or at a trot for 14 hours, run at top speed for 43 miles, or use an electrical vibrator for 94 hours! It really is much simpler not to eat that extra pat of butter than it is to try to "work it off" later.

A combination of diet and exercise is more effective than diet alone, if the exercises are chosen to aid the digestive process and improve the tone of the muscles as well as to increase the energy output. Useful exercises for this purpose include Nos. 20, 22, 23, and 24.

But what about "taking it off in the right places"? This is a different problem entirely. Many persons have dieted to the point of emaciation only to find that the same bulges still persist and become more noticeable after the general loss of body fat. If the bulges are a result of bony structure, nothing can be done about them except to disguise them as well as possible by the skillful choice of clothing.

The well-developed calf and thigh muscles of the ballet dancer, the tennis player, or the postman are the result of persistent exercise carried on over an extended period of time. These bulges are not fat, and no amount of diet will decrease them. If the bulges are muscle, they can be decreased only by decreasing the activity of the muscle to such an extent that muscle tone is lost and the fibers become sufficiently flabby to decrease in cross section. This sometimes happens during a prolonged illness or when a limb has been immobilized in a cast for a long period of time, but it can scarcely be recommended as a desirable procedure for the healthy individual.

However, many bulges are the result of poor body mechanics and poor posture. These bulges can be decreased by correcting the underlying cause. The double chin and the "dowager's hump" develop as a result of carrying the head in the forward position. They can be corrected by bringing the head back into the balanced position and carrying it erectly throughout all the waking hours.

Many thick ankles are the result of years of poor foot mechanics. If the foot is allowed to roll inward, throwing the weight of the body against the muscles and ligaments which pass down the inside of the ankle, the ankle appears much bulkier than it does when the weight is carried toward the outer border of the foot. Exercises to strengthen the stretched muscles on the inside of the ankle will be helpful in correcting mild pronation, such as Nos. 43 and 44. For more severe cases, it may be necessary to help the foot hold its corrected position with the aid of special shoes. Such shoes should be individually prescribed by an orthopedic surgeon, because poorly fitted "corrective" shoes may do much more harm than good.

The protruding abdomen and buttocks, with or without the accompanying "spare tire," are postural problems rather than weight problems. A simple experiment, entitled "How To Appear To Lose Ten Pounds in Ten Seconds," illustrates the importance of abdominal control in "reducing" bulges. Stand sideward before a full-length mirror. Let the shoulders sag, and relax the abdominal muscles in the posture of complete fatigue. Note how the thickness of the body increases from the waist downward. Clothing stretches taut over the abdominal bulge, and the body appears to be ten pounds heavier. Now straighten up in the extreme military posture with the shoulders thrown back and the abdomen "sucked in." Note that now the clothing is loose over the abdomen but is stretched tight over the protruding buttocks, and the body still appears to be thick and ungainly. Then bring the pelvic girdle into its supporting position directly under the trunk, lift the chest without "throwing it out," and stand as tall as possible without stretching. Note how the bulges have disappeared both fore and aft and the clothing hangs smoothly and without strain over the abdomen, buttocks, and hips. The diameter of the body has been decreased from two to four inches, and the whole body appears much slimmer. Not an ounce of weight has been lost, but the desired effect of *appearing* to lose ten pounds has been achieved.

Least valuable and most dangerous of all "reducing" exercises are those which attempt to beat the fat off in a specific location by pounding or slapping the offending part against the floor or other hard surface. The theory advanced in favor of this type of exercise is that it "breaks up" the fat and makes it easier for the body to absorb. Fat is not absorbed, it is consumed only as the body requires it for fuel, and in general the body selects first the fat most recently deposited for consumption when the need arises. Slapping or spanking the fat bulges produces no effect other than bruising the part and jarring the entire body.

Slow, controlled motion with the muscles under tension is much more effective in eliminating flabbiness and streamlining the body. Examples of such exercise are Nos. 36, 37, and 38.

Abdominal posture is discussed at length in Chapter 7. Exercises to improve the tone of the abdominal muscles and aid them in their work of controlling the postural balance are Nos. 10, 11, 12, and 13*b*.

Probably no two groups of people envy each other more than those who would like to lose weight and those who would like to gain weight. The too-thin individual, who would like to gain the ten pounds his neighbor wishes to lose, usually has the more difficult problem. His problem may be one of endocrine imbalance, specific deficiency of certain vitamins or minerals, disturbance of the digestive system, constipation, extreme tension, or overwork with insufficient rest. His problem is so often a medical one that the only sensible procedure is to seek the advice of a physician and determine the cause of his inability to gain weight. Exercise may be of value to him, but it must be chosen in line with the physician's diagnosis of his difficulty. He may need exercise for general stimulation of a sluggish digestive system, such as Nos. 19, 20, 23, and 32; he may need to adopt procedures for relaxation, described in Chapter 4; he may need abdominal exercise to tone up the abdominal muscles, such as Nos. 9 to 12; or he may need recreation to relieve his mind of its worries. But any course of action should be chosen only after the underlying cause of the inability to gain weight has been determined.

PROJECTS FOR FURTHER STUDY

1. Explain the statement, "A double chin is the other end of a dowager's hump."
2. For one week keep a chart of your own weight, weighing yourself as soon as you get up in the morning, immediately after breakfast, before dinner, after dinner, before going to bed, and as often during the day as you have the opportunity. Why is it difficult to answer the question, "What do you weigh?"
3. For one week make a list of the advertisements for "reducing" that you see in the newspaper and on television or hear on the radio. Classify them in terms of cost, method used, and results promised.
4. If you are not satisfied with your present weight, outline a sensible program for increasing or decreasing it.
5. Analyze a table d'hôte meal in some good restaurant or hotel. Count the number of calories it contains. Estimate the amount of exercise required to "work off" the calories in excess of your normal daily requirements.

Part III

THE CONSERVATION OF ENERGY

CHAPTER

7

The Balanced Posture: Standing

To MOST people the whole subject of posture is boring. From childhood they have been told, "Stand up straight!" "Keep your shoulders back!" "Stop lying in your chair, sit up like a lady!" Or, if they have experienced military training, "Attention!" The results of these admonitions have been negligible. Children learn to assume what they believe to be a "good" posture when commanded to do so, but the posture lasts no longer than the command.

Posture is a habit. It may be a good habit which contributes to the appearance and efficiency of the body; it may be a bad habit which spoils the appearance and makes the whole body inefficient. For good or ill, it *is* a habit which is acquired through long hours of conscious or unconscious practice. To say that posture is a habit is not the same thing as saying that it is automatic, uncontrolled, or uncontrollable. The position of the body and its parts, which is determined by muscle tonus and muscle action, is always under the control of the nervous system. This control is not always consciously maintained, but it exists nevertheless. The only unconscious and fully automatic posture is the total collapse which occurs in complete unconsciousness.

As the body assumes a given posture repeatedly, a habit of response is established in the neuromuscular system. This response becomes habitual, so that when the individual "takes his mind off" his posture, the neuromuscular system makes the familiar response because it is familiar and so "feels best" to the individual. This habitual posture may be like a pair of beloved and old house shoes. They may be sloppy, out of shape, down at the heels, and ill-fitting, but they are "comfortable" because the feel of them is so familiar to the foot. But if these "comfortable" old shoes are worn for eighteen holes of golf or for an afternoon of shopping, the feet, legs, and back soon make aching protest about the lopsided nonsupporting base which the faulty shoes provide. The habitual response of posture occurs whether the habit is bad or good, and many persons feel most "comfortable" in a posture which places a strain on every joint, because they have spent so much time in the strained position that any other response of the neuromuscular system is unfamiliar and, therefore, uncomfortable.

To place the body in a balanced, efficient, and graceful posture for five minutes a day, allowing it to resume an unbalanced, inefficient, and awkward position during all the rest of the waking hours, is a very ineffective procedure. The habit of years is not overcome in five minutes. The neuromuscular system must be given extensive and intensive reeducation over an extended period of time to establish a new habit of efficient response. This reeducation requires time, understanding, and persistence arising from a sincere desire to improve both the appearance and the efficiency of the body. Reading a book such as this one may supply the understanding, but the time and persistence must come from the person's own desire to change a poor habit into a better one.

Ten or fifteen minutes a day spent on "posture exercises" will produce very little in the way of improvement of posture. The exercises usually prescribed are intended to stretch the muscles of the chest wall and shorten the muscles which hold the scapulae in place, strengthen the muscles of the back of the neck and shoulders, and strengthen the muscles which keep the back erect. The theory is that if these muscles are kept shortened and under tension for a sufficient period of time, they will soon automatically hold the head up and the shoulders back against the weakened pull of the chest muscles. This theory is correct in the belief that muscles may be strengthened and shortened by exercise; it is incorrect in the belief that this shortening and strengthening will *automatically* correct the carriage of the head, shoulders, and trunk. The fallacy lies in thinking that the body responds only to intentional exercise. The truth is that the body is always exercising, and the effects of unintentional exercise are fully as great as or greater than those obtained from fifteen minutes a day of planned activity.

Take just one example. If the head is habitually carried in a forward position, the weight of the head constantly pulls on the muscles of the back of the neck, fatiguing and straining them. This strain is greatest at the point where the muscles cross the large vertebra at the base of the neck (seventh cervical vertebra). The body resents this strain and takes measures to reduce it by building up a fat pad to cushion and protect the muscles at this vulnerable point. In a few years this fat pad becomes prominent and the familiar "dowager's hump" appears. Attempts to counteract this constant pulling and stretching exercise, with five minutes of forcing the muscles of the neck and shoulders to contract, are futile. The effect of sixteen hours a day of stretching is far greater than the effect of five minutes of shortening and strengthening. The plan should be reversed. "Posture exercise" should be carried on for sixteen hours a day by holding the head in the balanced, unstretched position. Then five, ten, fifteen, or fifty minutes of allowing it to bob forward would have very little effect on the total result.

This concern about posture must extend beyond the limits of the standing position. The body is always in motion, and very seldom is there any occasion for it to assume the erect standing position without moving. Static posture has little significance except as a starting point for movement. The important problem of posture, then, is not how to balance the body efficiently in the erect standing position, but how to maintain this efficiency and grace as the body moves through the work and play of a twenty-four-hour day. This requires an understanding of the mechanics of movement and an ability to apply the principles of motion and efficiency to the expenditure and conservation of energy in the moving body. Since movement in a familiar situation also becomes habitual, the achievement of efficient *movement* also requires time and practice.

Strong muscles alone will not assure efficient motion as the body moves through all the daily activities which are its "posture exercises." In coordinated, graceful, and efficient movement the opposing muscles must be able to relax and lengthen readily and easily. If the efficient body is to move freely and easily in any anatomically possible direction, all muscles must be able to relax and lengthen, just as all muscles must be able to contract strongly and quickly.

The ability to feel this contraction and relaxation, to know what a muscle is doing, is called *kinesthetic perception*. This kinesthetic perception is also important to balanced and efficient movement, for unless the individual senses or feels the rightness or wrongness of a movement, he has no basis for correcting it or for trying to establish it as an habitual pattern. Kinesthetic perception is developed by consciously placing the body and its parts in a given position and "getting the feel" of it. This feeling of balance or imbalance, grace or awkwardness, serves as a constant guide to the body as it moves. As this feeling is developed, it, too, becomes habitual and semiconscious and serves as a potent force in making the daily activities serve as effective posture exercises for increasing the efficiency of the individual.

The fundamental concepts about modern posture exercise may be summarized as follows: (1) Every muscle should be

strong enough and have sufficient tone to perform its functions. (2) Every muscle should be relaxed enough to perform
its functions easily. (3) The joints to which the muscles are
attached should be flexible enough to make a full range of
movement possible. (4) Kinesthetic perception should be developed to such a degree that the body is uncomfortable unless
it performs each motion with a minimum of effort to produce
maximum results. (5) Posture exercise goes on through every
minute of life; it should be controlled to produce the best
results in strength, relaxation, flexibility, and efficiency.

These results can be achieved by any normal person who
has (1) an understanding of the process of movement and the
principles upon which efficient movement is based; (2) the
ability to control the movements of his own muscles; and (3)
the desire to acquire a balanced, effective posture—if that desire
is strong enough to cause him to apply the principles learned
to every activity of daily living over a sufficient period of time
to make their practice habitual.

The following chapters attempt to provide the information
necessary to an understanding of the principles of movement.
The desire, the application, and the ability must be provided
by the reader.

The human body is a mass of material. Like every other mass
of material it feels the pull of the force of gravity, which pulls
it down toward the earth and gives it the quality called *weight*.
It is not necessary to understand the "why" of gravity to understand its action; but an understanding of its pull on the human
body—or any material object—is necessary for an understanding of some of the most pertinent problems of posture.

Gravity may be thought of as a strong pulling force which
draws all material objects vertically downward toward the center of the earth, holding them in contact with the earth's surface
or with some other solid which in turn is in contact with the
earth's surface. This force acts on all parts of every object, but
it operates in such a way that for practical purposes it may be

considered as concentrating its pull on the weight center of the object. This weight center is called the *center of gravity*. The line which falls vertically downward from this center to the earth's surface is called the *line of gravity*.

Every object or mass of material has a center of gravity. This point is located in such a way that if a stiff sheet of paper were passed through that point, half the weight of the object would be on either side of the sheet. This is true regardless of the direction or starting place of the bisecting paper.

The existence of the center of gravity may be demonstrated by taking a piece of heavy cardboard of any shape, a bent hairpin or paper clip, and a piece of string with a key or other weight attached to one end.

Poke a hole at any point near the edge of the cardboard, making it large enough to insert the bent pin. Then take the string, which represents the line of gravity, and the key, which represents the pull, and slip the free end of the string over the bent pin. Hold the other end of the pin easily between the thumb and forefinger, allowing the cardboard, string, and key to hang from them without touching anything else. At first they will swing back and forth, but if the hand is held steady, this motion will stop, the string will hang straight down, and the cardboard will find its balance in such a position that exactly half of its weight is on each side of the vertical line of the string. Have someone lightly mark with a pencil the line of the string through the center of the cardboard.

Now take another point on the edge of the cardboard and make a new hole and repeat the entire process. The second pencil line will cross the first one at a point in the center of the cardboard. This point represents the center of gravity of the cardboard, the point through which the pull of gravity appears to act in pulling the cardboard down from its supporting hook. To test the truth of this statement, make a third hole in the edge of the cardboard, and repeat the string-hanging process. The string will lie across the point determined by the first two hangings. If the string is hung from any point on the edge of the cardboard, as it comes to rest it will lie across this point. The true center of gravity lies halfway through the thickness of the cardboard at the point where the string lines cross (Figure 7).

In the human body it is difficult to locate the center of gravity by any simple experiment like the one described above. When

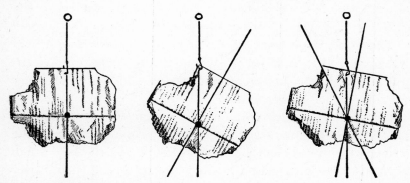

FIG. 7. The center of gravity of an irregular object may be located by suspending it in air.

the body is in the erect standing position with the arms hanging at the sides, the center of gravity lies about two inches above the hip joint, halfway through the body from front to back and halfway across the body from side to side. The location differs slightly in every individual, depending upon his body build and weight distribution; it also shifts as the body changes position throwing more weight forward, backward, or sideward; but this general description of the position of the center of gravity will be sufficient for discussing its relation to postural problems. The general location from top to bottom and from front to back is illustrated in Figure 8 by suspending from a supporting pin a cardboard outline of the human body in a variety of positions.

Find the location of the center of gravity of the body by approximately locating it with the fingers. Run the fingers

along the sides of the legs until the hip joint is located. About
the width of three fingers above the top of the hip joint is
the dividing line for body weight. Half the weight of the body
is above this level, and half of it is below. Since the two sides
of the body are very much alike, the center of gravity lies halfway through the body from side to side. From front to back the

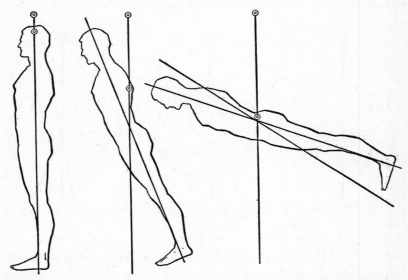

FIG. 8. The center of gravity of the body is slightly above the hip joint.

location is more difficult to determine, but for practical purposes the center of gravity may be considered as lying halfway
through the thickness of the body. This is the point through
which the force of gravity appears to act in pulling the body
downward toward the earth.

The question immediately arises, If this force is so strong
and pulls the body toward the earth, why does not the whole
body fall down into a heap on the ground? This is exactly what
does happen unless some solid object is placed between the
center of gravity and the ground. In the erect position the solid
legs are interposed between the center of gravity and the earth.
The downward pull of gravity encounters the resistance of two

solid pillars, which are themselves set firmly on the earth. The downward pull of gravity then serves to keep the body on the legs and the feet on the ground. In other words, all parts of the body are pulled firmly downward toward the supporting base, which is supplied by the feet, which rest on the ground. That part of the body which is in contact with the earth and through which the pull of gravity passes as it draws the body downward is called the *base of support*. If the center of gravity is directly above the base of support and solid structures lie between the center and the base, the body is *stable,* or *balanced,* and the pull of gravity is counteracted by the resistance of the supporting structures.

What happens if the center of gravity does not lie directly above the supporting base? The pull of gravity meets with no resistance, and the body falls until some part of it comes in contact with the ground in such a position that the part is between the ground and the center of gravity. Illustrate this by leaning forward from the ankles (stand facing a table or other solid object which can catch the weight of the body as it falls) with the body straight. As the body leans, the center of gravity moves forward toward the toes. As it passes the toes, there is no longer any supporting base, and the body falls forward until it is caught by placing the hands on the table. The hands on the solid table become a new point of support, and the body is supported by the feet and the hands. The line of gravity lies within the rectangle made by the feet and the hands, so forward motion is stopped because again the center of gravity lies directly above a base outlined by solid supporting structures.

Similarly, the body can lean sideward or backward from the ankles for only a short distance before the line of gravity moves outside the edge of the supporting base, balance is lost, and the body falls unless a new base is provided.

These experiments illustrate the first principle of body mechanics: *a body is stable, or balanced, when the center of gravity is over a supporting base.* Or, turning the statement around, whenever the line of gravity passes outside the area enclosed by the supporting base, balance is lost, and the body moves downward until a new base is provided which lies directly below the center of gravity (Figure 9).

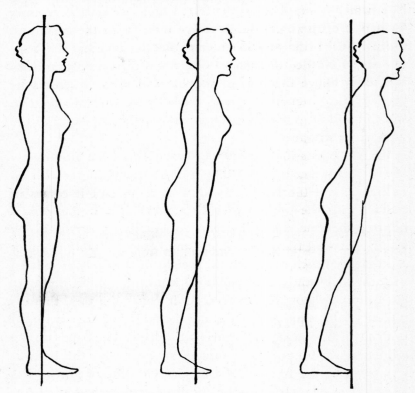

Fig. 9. A body is stable, or balanced, when the center of gravity is over the supporting base.

If the supporting base is very small, it is more difficult to maintain balance, for very slight movement may shift the center of gravity to such a position that the line of gravity passes beyond the edge of the base. Then balance is lost and the body falls until the necessary adjustments of center and base are made. From this it is evident that if the base is large, there is less chance that the body will be unbalanced (Figure 10).

However, the base may be large but the line of gravity may fall very near to one edge of it. This kind of balance is also precarious, for a small movement in the right direction may move the center of gravity past the edge of the base, and balance will again be lost. Regardless of the size of the base, it is easier to maintain balance if the line of gravity falls near the center of the supporting base, rather than close to the edge.

This all seems rather dry and technical, but it is on these principles that the whole concept of the balanced posture is

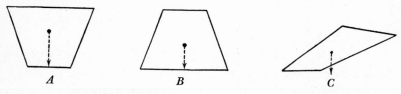

FIG. 10. *A* is easier to tip over than *B*; *C* is unstable and will fall.

built. These principles should be understood thoroughly before proceeding farther with an attempt to improve the posture of the body.

Stand with the feet parallel, three to six inches apart, with the weight of the body evenly distributed between them. The center of gravity lies directly above the space between the feet, and the line of gravity passes down between the legs. Note how the weight is borne equally by the legs and the pressure is felt equally on the soles of both feet.

Keeping the body straight, slowly lean forward from the ankles. Note the "falling forward" feeling as the line of gravity moves toward the toes. Note the feeling of pressure on the balls of the feet and the toes and the diminished pressure on the heels. The weight line is passing through the front part of the foot, and the heel is playing little or no part in the work of resisting the pull of gravity.

Shift the weight of the body to the right side. Note the decrease in pressure on the left foot and the increased pressure on the sole of the right foot. The line of gravity is now passing directly down through the right leg, and the left leg is relieved of its weight-bearing responsibility.

Return to the position in which the weight is felt evenly on both feet. Without shifting the body weight in any way, try to lift the right foot off the ground. It is impossible, because the pull of gravity is passing through the leg, and the foot must be kept on the ground to provide a supporting base which will permit the leg to resist this pull of gravity. To lift the right foot from the ground, it is first necessary to shift the weight of the body to the left leg to free the right leg from its supporting function.

With the weight on the left leg, lift the right foot from the ground. Note how much more difficult it is to maintain balance on one foot than it is on two. The supporting base is smaller, and it is more difficult to keep the line of gravity within the confines of the smaller base. Rise to the toes of the left foot, and note how the difficulty in maintaining balance increases. The base is now so small that a constant series of fine adjustments are necessary to keep the weight of the body so arranged that the line of gravity falls exactly within the narrow limits of the supporting base of the toes.

Lie flat on the floor. This is a very stable position in which balance is easy. The supporting base is now very large, and the line of gravity has no difficulty in staying within this big area. Get up on your hands and knees. This is the posture of the four-footed animals. Note how much more stable it is than the human posture. The hands and legs form four corners of a large base of support, and the center of gravity lies well within the limits of this large supporting base.

As man rose from the four-footed position and attempted to stand on two feet, he changed from a stable position in which his center of gravity was centered over a large supporting base to a position in which he attempted to balance a long, narrow body over a very small base. As a four-footed animal he had no difficulty in keeping his main line of gravity within the area of a large base; as a human being he had to solve the problem of keeping the center of gravity of his long, wobbly body over a ten- to fifteen-inch square. This is a difficult mechanical problem, and it is a tribute to the ingenuity of the human being that he solved it at all. As each child learns to stand erect, he must solve the problem for himself all over again, and in doing so he must learn to make adjustments in body position which give him the maximum amount of stability with the minimum amount of effort.

Up to this point the problem of balance has been made to appear simpler than it is by considering the body as a single mass of material. Unfortunately or fortunately, the body is not a solid structure but a jointed structure with many movable parts. As any part of the body moves, the total body acquires a new shape and a different distribution of its weight, and the center of gravity shifts with this new weight distribution in order to maintain the condition of having equal amounts of weight on all sides of it. This is illustrated in Figure 11 by placing the same outline figure in several positions and determining the location of the center of gravity in each position.

If the supporting base is not changed as parts of the body move forward, backward, or sideward, the center of gravity tends to shift forward, backward, or sideward, and the line of gravity may move outside of the area of the supporting base unless some other adjustment is made. This adjustment is made by allowing some other part of the body to move in the opposite direction from the original movement so that the weight is still evenly distributed about the original center. This adjustment is made more or less unconsciously as the body learns to maintain its balance and keep from falling.

Observe how these adjustments are made by moving parts of the body and note the result on the whole body. In the erect standing position raise both arms forward. Note how the upper back, and possibly the hips, move backward to balance the

weight of the arms. Swing both arms to the right side, and
note that the hips shift to the left to keep the body weight
centered over the feet. Bend forward from the waist. Note how
the legs slant to throw the hips and buttocks backward. Raise

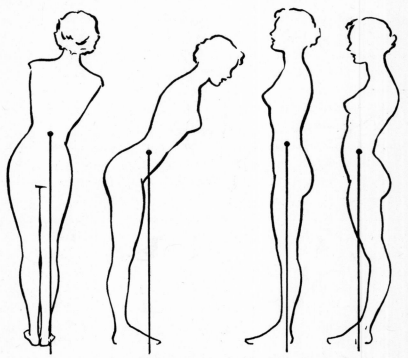

FIG. 11. The center of gravity shifts as the body position changes.

the right leg forward and note the shift in the position of the
supporting left leg and the instinctive motions of the arms as
they are raised to balance the body over the narrow base of
the left foot. Allow the abdomen and shoulders to slump forward in the posture of fatigue. Note how the hips and buttocks
move backward to compensate for the forward shift in weight.

Whenever one part of the body is moved away from the line
of gravity in any direction, an opposing part is moved in the
opposite direction to maintain balance. This compensated, or

zigzag, balance is somewhat precarious, since a slight shift in any of the parts involved in it may upset the entire structure (Figure 12).

Because the body is a jointed structure made up of a num-

FIG. 12. The skater maintains balance by matching each shift of weight in one direction by a corresponding shift in the opposite direction.

ber of separate movable parts tied together at the joints and held together by a covering of skin, the pull of gravity on each separate movable part must be considered, as well as the pull of gravity on the body as a whole. Each separate part has its own center of gravity, and each separate part rests on its own base. The head rests on the neck; the neck bones lie above the rest of the spinal column, which must support not only the neck but the weight of the head on top of the neck; the trunk is supported by the upper part of the legs, but must in turn support the weight of the neck, the head, the shoulder girdle, and the arms which hang from it; the upper part of the legs rest on the knee joint at the top of the lower legs, and these lower legs must support not only the thigh, but the trunk, the shoulder girdle and arms, the neck, and the head. The lower legs are supported by the ankle joints, which are supported by the bones of the feet, and the ankle joints must bear the combined weight of the lower legs, upper legs, trunk, shoulder girdle and arms, neck, and head. Gravity pulls through the center of each of these parts, through the common center of each combination of parts, and through the center of the entire structure (Figure 13).

If the center of gravity of the head does not lie directly above the supporting base of the neck, the force of gravity pulls the head downward. This pull is resisted by the muscles and ligaments of the neck, which keep the head from falling. There ensues a continuous tug of war between gravity—the pulling force which never rests—and the muscles and ligaments of the back of the neck, which cannot let go but which do become fatigued and stretched from the constant strain placed upon them. The unbalanced position of the head threatens the balance of the entire body unless some compensation is made by shifting some other part of the body backward to equalize the weight thrown forward by the head (Figure 14).

The center of weight of the shoulder girdle with its dependent arms must be centered over the spinal column, which provides its support. The center of gravity of the trunk, shoulder girdle, neck, and head combined must lie directly above the pelvic girdle, which in turn must rest squarely upon the supporting legs, or again muscles and ligaments must work constantly to offset the pull of gravity downward, which will unbalance the entire body.

Total balance is maintained with a minimum expenditure of energy by balancing each movable body part securely on its own supporting base, so that the pull of gravity on it serves

only to hold it firmly in line with the rest of the body. Total
balance is maintained by a wasteful expenditure of energy
when any part is allowed to move forward, backward, or side-

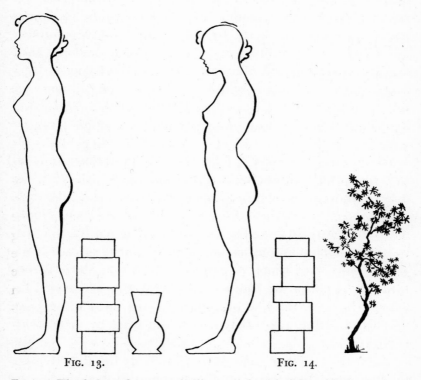

FIG. 13.   FIG. 14.

FIG. 13. The balanced posture is like a stack of building blocks, each set
squarely on the block beneath it.

FIG. 14. The unbalanced posture zigs and zags.

ward so far that its own partial center of gravity lies outside
the limits of the base which supports the part. When any part
projects beyond its supporting base, the pull of gravity tends
to drag it farther downward toward the earth, and this pull
must be combated by an equally strong pull in the opposite
direction exerted by the muscles and ligaments which hold the
part in place. In addition, another part of the body must be

moved out of line with its base in the opposite direction to maintain the total balance of the body. This compensated, or zigzag, balance is not only energy-consuming but unstable, because it is easily upset by the shift of any of the parts involved. This posture resembles the many-branching Christmas tree, which is easily upset by the slightest breeze or touch unless it is held in position by heavy weights at the base. Each branch projects beyond the base and must be balanced by a branch on the other side which projects an equal distance. A light touch or small weight applied to one of these projecting branches is sufficient to topple the whole tree (Figure 14).

The balanced posture is like a stack of building blocks set squarely one on top of the other. Gravity pulls downward on each block, but because the center of gravity of each block lies directly above the supporting base of the block below, the stack does not fall but is held firmly together by its own weight. The blocks may be moved slightly out of line, but the pile will continue to stand as long as the center of gravity of each block and the combined center of gravity of all blocks above it continue to lie above the base of support. If they are moved far enough to cause the line of gravity to pass outside the base, they will collapse unless they are held in place by some resisting force.

When the center of each part of the body lies directly over the base which supports it, gravity becomes a force which pulls the body together. When any part projects out of line and is totally or partially unsupported at its base, gravity becomes a force to pull the part farther out of line, and this pull must be combated by the ligaments and muscles which hold the part to the body. The secret, then, of maintaining total body balance with a minimum expenditure of energy is to cooperate with the pull of gravity, to work *with* gravity, not *against* it.

Balanced posture is achieved by carrying each body part in such a position that it balances as securely as possible on the part below which acts as its base of support. The direction and distance which each part can move over its base is determined by the construction of the joints which attach the part to its supporting base. Movements in some directions can be made easily and occur frequently; other movements are made less easily and seldom occur; still other movements are quite impossible and are of no concern in the study of the balanced posture.

In attempting to balance the parts of the body for economical posture, it is best to concentrate on those motions which are most likely to take place. For example, the head and neck may be bent forward easily and over a fairly long distance. It is difficult to bend the head and neck very far backward. If the head moves out of its balanced position on the neck, it is much more likely to fall forward than it is to fall backward. The problem of balancing the head and neck on the shoulders is primarily one of keeping them from falling forward and exerting a pull on the muscles of the back of the neck.

Before going on to the experimental process of finding the balanced position, it seems desirable to restate the principles which have been developed and illustrated as they apply to the parts of the body. They are the same as those for the body as a whole, but because the jointed structure is more complex, the principles which apply must be stated more fully:

1. Any part of the body is stable and balanced when the center of gravity of that part, and the parts above it, is over the supporting base.
2. If the line of gravity passes near the edge of the supporting base, balance is easily disturbed. Therefore balance is most easily maintained when the line of gravity passes near the *center* of the supporting base.
3. As the line of gravity of one part moves beyond the edge of the supporting base, the balance of the whole body will be lost unless some other part is moved out of line in the opposite direction, or unless an opposing force is applied to maintain the body in the unbalanced position.

The "balancing act" which is described below is based on the application of these principles. Bearing in mind the fact that balance is easily lost when the line of gravity lies too close to the edge of the supporting base, an attempt is made to find a position in which the respective gravity lines have ample room to move in all directions without going beyond the edge of the base. In the position of maximum balance there will be a *margin for movement* in all directions at each joint.

Stand with the feet a comfortable distance apart. Move them close together and notice the feeling of insecurity which the narrow base induces. Place the feet far apart. The base is now wider, but the legs slant outward so that the weight of the body is carried toward the inner edge of the knee joint and the ankle joint. Neither position gives a good base for balance, the one because it is too small, the other because the weight-bearing legs are not in line with the body and because the range of motion for the legs is limited to either side. Take the position halfway between these two extremes, with the feet a comfortable distance apart so that the legs come straight down under the body.

From this position, move the toes outward into the "toe-out" position. This increases the size of the base by increasing the angle between the feet, but the advantage from the larger base is less important than the strain on the ankle joint caused by having the weight of the body borne by the inner sides of the joints. Try the "toe-in" position. The size of the base is reduced and the knee joints are turned in to allow the foot and leg to rotate inward. Again, neither extreme position of the feet is desirable as a base for balancing the body. The feet should be in an approximately parallel position, a few inches apart, to give the most support with the least amount of strain on the joints and muscles of the feet and legs.

With the feet in this parallel position, rock the body backward and forward from the ankle joint, noting how the pressure on the soles of the feet moves first back toward the heels and then up toward the toes. For maximum support the pressure should be distributed evenly over the heel and ball of each foot, and the body should be able to rock either backward or forward without endangering its balance. Rock the body backward and forward a few times and gradually let it come to rest over the feet in this balanced position.

Keeping the feet flat on the floor and the back erect, bend the knees forward. As they bend note the pull exerted by the muscles of the lower leg and thigh to hold the body upright in this unbalanced position with the upper and lower leg making an angular instead of a straight support for the upper body. Straighten the knees, pushing them backward as far as they will go. They will move backward only slightly, then the joint locks and no further motion is possible. This position leaves no margin for movement backward. Slightly bend the knees, then straighten them forcibly. Do this several times and gradually find the position in which the knees are neither bent nor pushed backward. This slightly relaxed position of the knees gives maximum support and still leaves room for the knee joints to move backward if the need for such motion arises.

The hip joints permit of much motion forward, but this big forward motion is not likely to occur in the erect position, since it throws the entire weight of the trunk forward and makes balance very difficult and fatiguing. But the trunk moves easily forward on these main hinges of the body, and a slight forward bend frequently occurs. Bend slightly forward from the hip joints, then move the entire trunk backward from the hip joints as far as possible. Note how the knee joints immediately lock in the backward position as the center of gravity of the trunk moves backward. Move the trunk backward and forward slightly at the hip joints, feeling the movement of the legs, knees, and ankle joints as the legs attempt to compensate for the forward or backward position of the trunk. Bring the trunk into the position which makes it possible for the legs to remain straight down under it with the knee and ankle joints relaxed and with the pressure equally distributed between the heels and balls of the feet.

Be sure this balance is also effected from side to side. Shift the weight to the right leg, then back to the left leg. Then find the balanced position in which the weight is borne equally by both legs.

To bring the pelvis into the balanced position directly under the trunk which it is designed to support, first rotate the pelvis through its entire range of motion forward and backward. With the back of the pelvis sloping backward and outward, note how the trunk is deprived of support in front. Note also how the entire body weight shifts backward, locking the knee joints and putting the weight pressure on the heels. With the back of the pelvis sloping downward and forward, note the tendency to bend the knees and to round the upper back in order to compensate for the unbalanced position of the pelvis and abdomen. Move the pelvic girdle backward and forward a few times, finally placing it in the position directly under the trunk from which it can move either forward or backward with ease. Try to get the feeling of having the trunk "sit down" in this pelvic basin, so that the abdominal viscera receive maximum support from the bony and muscular walls of the pelvis (Figure 15).

Raise the chest high and force it forward. Note how the upper back is forced backward to balance the chest, increasing the inward curve of the lower part of the spine. Let the chest collapse to its lowest and most sunken position. Note how the abdomen protrudes and the head is brought forward beyond the balanced line. Move the chest between these two positions, allowing it to come to rest in a position halfway between these two extremes. Get the feeling of pulling *up*, not out, at the top of the flat bone to which the ribs are attached (the sternum). Place a finger and thumb in the hollow at the top of the sternum and gently lift the chest upward. Pull it as high as possible and then allow it to relax slightly. In this position the upper part of the spinal column, to which the ribs are attached, is almost straight, and the ribs hang from it in a position which makes motion up and out, in and down, easy and economical.

Raise the shoulders toward the ears. Drop them down as far as possible. Move them forward and backward and note the resulting muscle pulls and tensions across the back. The base of support of the shoulder girdle is very complex, and the weight is borne indirectly at several points. The clavicles are joined to the sternum in front, and the sternum derives its support indirectly from the rib cage which is attached to the spinal column in back. The scapulae have no joint with the spinal column but are attached to the back wall of the rib cage with flat muscles which hold them in place. The head of the upper arm fits into the joint between the clavicle and the scapula on either side. Muscles attached to the upper arm-bone cross the shoulder joint and attach to the clavicle, the scapula, and the vertebrae of the neck and upper back. This complicated support makes the shoulder girdle something like a wooden yoke used for carrying water buckets, the arms taking the place of the dangling buckets. The yoke gets its support from the spinal column. If it is carried too far forward it tends to bend the body backward. It is carried most easily in the mid-position with the buckets

Fig. 15. FPT means fine posture.

hanging straight down with their weight line parallel with the line of the spinal column. Find this position for the shoulder girdle and arms by moving them forward, then pushing them back as far as possible. Move back and forth between these two positions, and allow the shoulders to come to rest halfway between them. This position can also be found by hunching the shoulders up toward the ears, then allowing them to drop down easily.

Finally, find the balance point for the head. Raise the chin and force the head backward. Then allow the head to drop forward until the chin almost touches the top of the sternum. In both positions strain is felt on the muscles of the neck. Move the head back and forth between these two positions, gradually decreasing the amount of movement in each direction. Find the position midway between "nose in the air" and "chin on the chest." Let the head come to rest in this position. Identify the *feeling* of having the head set squarely on top of the column of the neck, with the chin making approximately a right angle with the neck in front, and the bulge of the back of the head extending beyond the line of the neck in back for balance. In this position the weight-bearing line from the head passes directly down the column of the neck, and the weight is borne by the spinal column.

Actually this whole procedure of finding balance points is not a balancing process, for balance has been destroyed at each joint by the experimental movement of the body parts above the joint. It has been done as a means of developing kinesthetic perception, of "getting the feel" of putting the body in unbalanced and balanced positions. Concentration on each of these movements has developed a feeling of tension, and the resulting posture is far from comfortable.

Relax, and let the whole body slump. Then quickly put the body back in balance by mentally pulling up through the top of the head and down through the entire line of the spinal column. Get the feeling of being suspended from a hook in the top of the head, with a heavy tail hanging down from the end of the spine. The tail should pull straight down. Do not let it stick out in back or curl down between the legs. Let it pull straight down against the upward pull of the hook on top of the head.

Slump again, and quickly and easily return to the balanced

position by bringing the top of the head up until it just touches, but does not support, an imaginary bucket of water hanging directly overhead. Do not strain or stretch, but reach easily with the top of the head. Mentally check the possibilities for movement at each joint. Is the weight evenly distributed over the soles of the feet? Is forward and backward movement possible at the ankle joints? Are the knees relaxed so that they can be pushed backward without strain? Is the trunk balanced on the hip joint, neither toppling forward nor bending backward? Is the pelvic girdle directly under the trunk, with the trunk resting securely in its basin? Can the pelvic girdle move backward and forward easily? Is the chest raised so that it can either extend farther or sink deeper? Are the shoulders hanging easily from their support? Can they move forward, backward, up, or down with ease? Is the head set squarely on the neck with no strain on the muscles either in front or in back? In brief, is there *freedom to move* at every joint?

There should be no tension and no feeling of being in a "held" position when the best possible balance has been achieved. It is a position of ease, for there is freedom to move in each anatomically possible direction at every joint. This freedom to move makes the balanced posture a *position of safety,* for the body is able to "give" in any direction to absorb the force of a blow or an unexpected movement. If there is no "give" to take up the force of the blow, the ligaments and tendons will be stretched and torn. If there is even a small amount of freedom to move, the body can adjust to the shock or movement and it will do no harm.

Dr. Goldthwait, one of the greatest of orthopedic surgeons and teachers of body mechanics, has graphically described the importance of the freedom to move: *

Any joint, no matter how much or how little motion it may have, is in danger of being injured if, for any reason, its motion

* Joel E. Goldthwait *et al.: Body Mechanics in Health and Disease.* Philadelphia: J. B. Lippincott Company, 1941. Pp. 30–31.

is forced beyond the normal range. For purposes of description
we can compare a joint to the hinge on the door of an automobile. Automobile doors all have stops to prevent the door from
swinging too far open; these stops are like the ligaments. Many
of us have had the experience of seeing an automobile door left
open so that the stop strap, or ligament, is tight, and then pushed
still farther open. The result is a broken strap, a broken hinge,
or a broken door, or all three. The potential reason for this
accident is that the door was at one extreme of its motion and
that, the stop strap, or ligament, being tight, there was no so-
called factor-of-safety motion left. The actual reason was the
blow on the door; the same blow, if the door had not been at
one extreme of its range of motion, and so had a factor-of-safety
motion, might not have caused any damage. The significant fact
here, therefore, from the point of view of safety or health, is not
the blow but the position of the door when it was struck, in
relation to the limits of the possible range of motion in its hinges.

The balanced posture, with its factor-of-safety motion, places
the body and its parts in a position of safety with its ligaments
and muscles unstretched and, therefore, ready to act to absorb
the shocks or jars which occur in standing on a jolting streetcar,
stepping down suddenly from a curbing, or being pushed about
in a crowd.

The balanced posture, which makes full and effective use of
the force of gravity by aligning all parts so that the pull is
directly downward through supporting structures, reduces to
a minimum the work done by the muscles in maintaining the
body in an erect position. The muscles and ligaments around
each joint serve only to hold the part in place, cooperating with
the pull of gravity instead of constantly having to work against
it. The less work muscles have to do, the less energy they expend and the less fatigue they experience. The balanced posture
is, therefore, the economical posture. That it is also the most
attractive and graceful posture is only an additional dividend.

If this balanced posture is examined for weak points to discover the places at which it is most likely to go to pieces, it will be noted at once that the hip joints are the main hinges of the body and the ones most likely to be distorted by unbalanced weight distribution or lack of control. In the erect posture the position of the hip joints and the pelvic girdle is controlled primarily by the muscles of the abdomen and the buttocks (gluteal muscles). If these muscles have poor tone, or the ability to control them is inadequate, they are unable to perform easily their function of controlling the position of the pelvic girdle. When this is true, balanced posture is almost impossible to achieve. If this control is lacking, the posture quickly becomes unbalanced, and the zigzag erect position is maintained by allowing the body weight to "hang from the ligaments."

To emphasize the truth of the statement that abdominal and gluteal control are the fundamental elements of the balanced posture, experiment with various positions of the pelvic girdle and abdominal wall. Assume the position of "fatigue slump" with abdomen protruding, pelvic girdle rotated so that the tail bone points backward, chest sunken, and shoulders and head forward. Now without changing the position of the pelvic girdle or the abdomen, try to bring the head up to the balanced position. Try to raise the chest to its easy-action position. Try to straighten the shoulders so that they hang easily from the spinal column. These "corrections" are difficult and made with much discomfort, so long as the pelvic girdle and abdominal wall are in bad position.

Assume the sway-backed posture with the hips thrown backward. Without changing the position of the pelvic girdle, try to relax the shoulders and let them hang easily. Try to balance the head comfortably on the neck. Try to unlock the knees. Again these adjustments are difficult or impossible with the pelvic girdle in the unbalanced position.

Now reverse the experiment. Bring the pelvic girdle into the balanced position with the abdominal wall held flat (but not sucked in) by easy muscle control. While holding this balanced pelvic-abdominal position, attempt to push the head forward. Try to push the shoulders forward or backward. Try to lock the knees in the backward position. Rock the weight forward over the toes and backward over the heels. Each of these unbalanced positions is difficult and uncomfortable to maintain with the pelvic girdle in the balanced position and with the abdominal wall under control.

These experiments serve to demonstrate that the keynote of the balanced posture is good abdominal-pelvic-gluteal control. This control can be achieved only if the abdominal and gluteal muscles are kept in good tone and kinesthetic perception of the action of these muscles is developed. For some individuals, this will require planned exercise for the abdominal and gluteal muscles; for others, the necessary tone and control can be maintained by using the muscles correctly as they carry on their daily activities. Abdominal exercises are described in the Appendix. Numbers 9, 10, 11, 12, 13*b*, and 22 are well suited to the development of tone and control in relation to the balanced posture.

This recognition of the major role played by good abdominal-pelvic-gluteal control in the attainment of the balanced posture greatly simplifies the whole postural problem. If this important part of the body is maintained in the balanced position, most of the other postural problems will either solve themselves or will need only minor adjustments. Dr. Kathryn Wells, an outstanding teacher of body mechanics, has reduced the problem of the balanced posture to one simple sentence: "Keep your feet under your pelvis, and your pelvis under your trunk." This is easy to remember, and its remembrance makes checking on the balanced posture simple. If the supporting base of the entire body and the supporting base of the trunk are in line, the posture is reasonably well balanced. If the pelvic girdle falls ahead of or in back of the feet, or if the trunk tends to fall ahead of or in back of the pelvic girdle, then the body is out of line and no correction is possible until basic correction of alignment is made.

In this day of alphabetical agencies and slogans, it may be easier to reduce this sentence still further to the six letters, FPT—MFP. Translated, this reads: Feet under the pelvis, pelvis under the trunk—means fine posture (Figure 15).

Now apply this slogan to get more practice in kinesthetic perception and in transforming a faulty posture into a balanced one. Assume the fatigue slump posture, and note how the pelvic girdle falls backward of the feet and the abdomen forward of the pelvic girdle. Correct this posture by bringing the feet, pelvis, and trunk in line. Assume the sway-backed, locked-knee position. Note again that the trunk makes an S curve above the pelvic girdle, while the legs slant backward away from the heels to meet the protruding pelvic girdle. Correct this posture by bringing the feet, pelvis, and trunk back into line. Do the same for the back-on-the-heels posture, the forward lean, the weight-on-one-leg-with-the-opposite-hip-stuck-out posture. In each position the basic principle of FPT is violated. Each posture may be corrected to the position of balance by applying FPT.

This chapter has been long and contains many tedious details. These details seem necessary in order to present, first, the reasons for attempting to achieve a balanced posture in terms of economy, efficiency, and grace; second, the mechanical principles which underlie the attainment of a balanced posture, so that the process of balancing a jointed body may be understood; and third, the procedures which may be used in attaining and maintaining balance. The most important factor in balancing posture must be supplied by the individual—the desire to acquire the habit of balancing the body parts in such a way as to relieve muscles from strain, the desire to acquire the kinesthetic perception of muscle action required to achieve this balance, and the persistence to practice placing the body in the balanced position frequently enough to establish the

new neuromuscular pattern and make it familiar and, therefore, comfortable. This is the hard part, for it is difficult to blot
out an old, familiar pattern in the neuromuscular system—but
unless this is accomplished, no permanent improvement in postural balance will be made.

This practice should be carried on at intervals throughout
the day without interfering in any way with other activities.
Walking through a doorway to enter or leave a room may serve
as a cue to remember FPT. Standing on a crowded streetcar,
absorbing the jolting and swaying motion, is a good time to
practice FPT. The act of rising from a chair to the standing
position may serve as a reminder of FPT. Standing before a
class to make a report, confidence and assurance will increase if
FPT is first observed. This incidental practice is the most important kind, for it relates the balanced posture to the necessary,
important, or interesting activities of living, and the balanced
posture soon becomes such an integral part of those activities
that it is assumed unconsciously as the most comfortable basis
for meeting all situations.

PROJECTS FOR FURTHER STUDY

1. In street clothes, stand before a full-length mirror. Assume a
   number of different postures, varying from the fatigue slump to
   the extreme military stance. Note how each change of posture
   affects your appearance. Note how each change affects the way
   your clothing appears to fit. Find the posture in which your
   clothes fit best and in which you make your best appearance.
   Check this posture for FPT.
2. For one week, at least ten times a day, mentally check your posture to determine whether or not you are maintaining the posture
   you decided was most becoming. Each time try to do it by "getting the feel" of it rather than by looking in a mirror.
3. Stand in balanced FPT posture. Gradually let yourself slump
   to an unbalanced posture. Return to the FPT posture. Repeat

the process several times, trying to identify the points of strain in the unbalanced posture.

4. For one day consciously observe the posture of the people around you. Write a brief paper on "Postures I Have Seen."

5. While standing in line, in the cafeteria, on the streetcar, while waiting to cross the street, or anywhere that you may be standing for a few minutes, check your posture for FPT. At the same time, check yourself for tension. Relax, and get in balance.

6. Explain the statement, The basic posture exercises are abdominal exercises.

CHAPTER

8

The Balanced Posture: Walking

THE LIVING body seldom remains stationary for any length of time. It moves, constantly changes positions, and in assuming new positions it is confronted with the problem of maintaining balance with each new arrangement of the body parts. The static balanced posture is not maintained as the body moves; it is important only as the base from which movement is begun. The more difficult problem of posture is that of maintaining balance in a structure of which all parts are in motion.

Body locomotion (walking, running, skipping, dancing, moving from place to place) is subject to the same mechanical principles as those which govern the working of any machine. If these principles are understood, the individual may take advantage of them to make locomotion an easy and efficient process. Any attempt to move in defiance of these laws produces motion which is strained, awkward, and inefficient, and energy is wasted.

Any object or body which is stationary, stable, or at rest will remain in that position unless force is applied to set it in motion. The body follows this law, and it will remain in any stable position unless force is applied to move it. This law is not so simple as it first appears to be, however, for the object does not always move in the direction in which the force is applied. If the force is applied so that it pushes or pulls directly through the center of gravity, the object will move in the direction of the pushing or pulling force. But if the force is applied above, below, or on either side of the center of gravity, the object will move in the general direction of the force; it will also rotate about its own center of gravity and may move diagonally instead of straight forward.

Illustrate the truth of this principle by pushing on the corner of a table. Note how the table tends to turn with the push, rotating about its own center and moving away in a diagonal direction. Push against the top of the back of a chair, above its center of gravity. Note how the chair tips forward as it moves and tends to topple over. In neither instance was the desired objective accomplished of moving the object straight forward. If it is to reach its original destination, further energy must be expended to straighten it out on its course and correct the deviation caused by failing to push directly through the center of gravity.

How does this apply to the locomotion of the human body? What pushes the body around? The answer, of course, is that the body is a self-propelling machine and must itself supply the force which causes it to move. This is a complicated process, since the push or pull must come from within the body which is to be moved, and the force must be supplied by the contraction or extension of the muscles of the body.

The muscles of the body are attached to the bones of the skeletal framework. As noted in Chapter 2, the muscles of the arms and legs are attached to two or more bones, which are held together by a joint. One end of the muscle is attached at some point to the bone above the joint and the other end is attached at some point to the other bone below the joint. When the muscle contracts, it shortens, and the two bones move toward each other. Since they are tied together by the joint at their adjacent ends, the only motion possible is that of changing the *angle* between them. In other words, the force of the contracting muscle pulls the two bones together in an angular motion. When the muscle on the opposite side of the joint contracts, the bones are pulled back into line (Figure 16).

This angular motion of rotating one or both bones about the fixed point of the joint is the only motion possible for the bones of the arms, legs, shoulder girdle, and pelvic girdle. If the body is to move forward instead of in circles, the problem of transforming this circular or angular motion into translatory or straightforward motion must be solved.

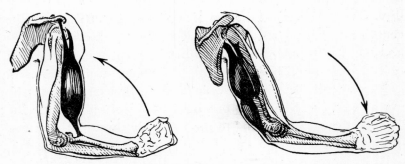

Fig. 16. When a muscle contracts, the angle between two bones is increased or decreased.

The solution is not difficult. Work it out with a ruler. Hold one end in the fingers and rest the other end on the table. Push the top end over a few inches, while the bottom remains fixed. This is angular motion. Now hold the top steady and push the bottom forward. This is a second angular motion in the opposite direction. If the two angles are equal, the ruler will now be in the same position it was at first, but it will have progressed across the table. Angular motion has been transformed into translatory motion (Figure 17).

One difficulty was encountered in the above experiment. The top end of the ruler had to be raised slightly to allow the lower end to swing forward. This difficulty could be solved by putting a joint in the middle of the ruler and allowing it to bend (a second angular motion) sufficiently to permit the lower end to clear the table (Figure 18).

Illustrate this phenomenon using legs instead of the ruler. Stand with both feet together. Swing the right leg forward, bending the left knee slightly to lower the body sufficiently so that the right heel may strike the floor. Straighten the left knee and extend the left ankle, pushing the top of the right leg forward until it is again directly over the foot. As the right foot

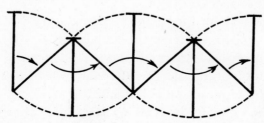

FIG. 17. Angular motion may be transformed into translatory motion.

supports the weight, bend the left knee and ankle slightly to shorten the left leg and permit it to swing forward until it is again beside the right leg and the weight is evenly distributed on both feet.

The problem is solved. The body has been propelled directly forward by combining a series of circular or angular motions.

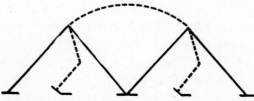

FIG. 18. A jointed stick can be made to move in a straight line by successive angular movements.

The force has been supplied by contracting and extending the muscles of the legs, which moved the bones in an angular pattern. Alternately the legs swing forward, the knee joints and ankle joints are flexed and extended, the weight is shifted from one leg to the other, and locomotion is achieved. Each separate motion is initiated by the contraction of muscle, and through this contraction energy is spent and force is exerted. If the motion is sufficient just to accomplish its purpose, and if the force of the muscle contraction is applied in exactly the right direction to move the part to its next position, then the walk is efficient and economical. If too much force is used, or if it is expended in the wrong direction, the walk becomes labored, awkward, and uneconomical.

Walk slowly about the room "getting the feel" of the movements and weight shifts required. Note how the front foot strikes the floor, heel first; how the back foot pushes the body over the front foot, transferring the body weight to the leading foot; how the hips move forward and backward as first one leg and then the other leads. Walking is a highly complicated coordination. Marvel at the fact that infants manage to accomplish it at all. Recognize that this complex of coordinations permits many variations, and begin to understand why so many people fail to perform it gracefully, smoothly, or efficiently. A variation in any single motion affects the performance of all the others. If the foot is pointed outward as it is set down, the whole body follows the lead of the foot and the body moves in a zigzag path instead of straight ahead. If the pushing foot extends too forcibly, the whole body tends to topple forward, and the weight must be caught suddenly and heavily on the leading foot. If the weight is shifted too far to the side as it is transferred to the leading foot, the hips sway sideward. Each of these common faults breaks some part of the law of applying the force directly through the center of gravity in the direction in which motion is desired, or the principle of using only enough force to produce the desired result. Each of these faults must be paid for by additional motion in the opposite direction or by force applied to stop the motion.

The forces which cause the body to move are all derived from the flexion and extension of muscles, but all muscles are not equally adapted to the task of supplying such forces. Some muscles are large and strong, others are small and relatively weak. If a weak muscle is called upon to do a heavy task, it will at first succeed by throwing all its fibers into contraction. But as the task continues these fibers become fatigued, and as they fatigue they become less efficient and are less able to perform their function. If a strong muscle is used for the same task, it will use only a part of its fibers at a time, alternating fibers in such a way that part of them rest while the others work. The strong muscle will thus be able to continue for a longer period of time and at less fatigue cost than a weak muscle, since the fibers of a strong muscle have alternating periods of work and recovery. To perform any continuous task efficiently, the strongest muscles available for the task should be used.

In the human body, the strongest muscles are those found in the legs and thighs. These muscles are large, strong, and relatively tireless in their task of moving the body weight about. These are the muscles which should be used for walking. It may sound extremely obvious to say that the leg muscles should be used for walking, but, strangely enough, many people make relatively little use of the legs for this purpose. They impart motion to their bodies by using the muscles of their backs, using the strong legs only for purposes of support.

Walking is a series of balances lost and found. The body starts from a stable, balanced position. The center of gravity is moved ahead until it passes beyond the original base of support, at which point balance is lost. By moving the legs appropriately (and quickly enough), a new base of support is provided and balance is found again in a new position. This alternate losing and regaining of balance may be done in many different ways. Basically these ways may be classified under two general descriptions: (1) walking with the back, and (2) walking with the legs.

The difference between these two types of locomotion may best be understood by experiencing them. Stand with the right foot ahead in the normal walking stride. Allow the head, shoulders, and trunk to move forward over the leading leg. Feel the line of gravity move toward the toes and experience the sensation of falling forward. As the line of gravity reaches the toes, the left leg moves up quickly and advances to catch the weight of the body and to provide a new base of support to keep the body from falling. Because gravity is already pulling the body forward and downward, the step will be hurried and heavy as it stops this forward and downward motion. The left leg did not push off, for no weight was on it; it only moved hurriedly to get under the body again and stop its descent. No great amount of energy was used to get the left leg forward, since it did not have to move the body weight, but energy was required to stop the body weight in its downward fall and to overcome the acceleration which the pull of gravity had imparted to the body weight. This energy was spent hurriedly and the movement was difficult to control; as a result the step was heavy and the jar was transmitted to the entire body. Dr. Arthur Steindler has described this kind of walk as "a series of catastrophes narrowly averted," for the body always tends to be ahead of the supporting base of the legs, and if at any moment the legs fail to catch up with the body, the walker experiences the catastrophe of falling flat on his face.

This is the "gorilla type" of walking, with the heavy upper body always forward in an essentially unbalanced position (Figure 19). This is not dangerous for the gorilla, for he has long arms which reach to the ground and may be used as an auxiliary base of support ahead of the legs. For the human being, who has no such long arms with which to support himself, this walk may be truly catastrophic. The center of gravity is constantly moving ahead of the base of support, so that gravity exerts a strong downward pull on the unsupported trunk, putting a strain on the linked-chain spinal structure and the relatively weak muscles which hold each vertebra to the vertebrae above and below it. Gravity also exerts a pull on the unsupported abdominal viscera, forcing the heavy organs downward and forward against the sagging abdominal wall. The chest tends to be collapsed, and the arms, head, and shoulders fall ahead of their bases of support, with gravity pulling them downward. Not only is the whole body in a weak, unbalanced position, needing only a slight push to send it sprawling, but damage is being done to vital organs and muscles by the constant pull of gravity. In this position much of the energy consumed in walking is spent by the muscles of the back and trunk; the

FIG. 19. The gorilla "walks with his back."

legs exert no push but merely swing under the body to keep it from falling, and then all the muscles of the leg must contract sharply and suddenly to stabilize the leg as it receives the body weight and stops it in its downward fall. "Walking with the back" is ungraceful, but, more important, it is inefficient because the muscles of the trunk are used to accomplish with difficulty and danger what could be accomplished easily and safely by the strong muscles of the legs; and the muscles of the legs are used unproductively and at a disadvantage only to *stop* the forward-downward motion of the body.

To experience "walking with the legs," begin by assuming the balanced standing posture, with the pelvic girdle directly over the supporting legs and the trunk balanced securely in the pelvic girdle. Shift the weight slightly to the left, then swing the right leg forward *ahead of the body.* As the right heel strikes the floor, begin the push-off with the left foot and leg, transferring the balanced body to the support of the right leg. Swing the left leg easily under the body, which is supported by the right leg, and place it ahead of the body ready to receive the weight from the push-off of the right foot. The legs are now

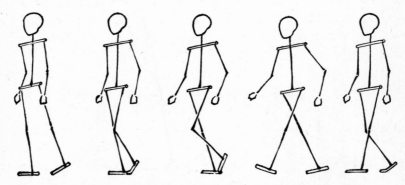

FIG. 20. Always prepare a new base before leaving the old.

supplying the energy for walking. A new base of support is prepared before the body is unbalanced by being pushed off its old base, and the leading foot is ready to receive the body weight easily and gradually with no strain or jar (Figure 20). This walk may be described as "leading with the thigh" in contrast to "leading with the head" in the unbalanced gorilla walk. The leading leg is always parallel with or in advance of the trunk, so that a new base of support is always ready to receive the body weight, and there is no phase of insecurity or imbalance while the center of gravity passes its old base of support. The trunk is always balanced in the pelvic basin, and the abdominal muscles and head and neck are always securely balanced and not dragged forward by the pull of gravity. With the swinging leg well ahead and ready to receive the body weight, and with the upper body in line with the axis of the back leg, the supporting and pushing leg is able to apply its force directly through the center of gravity along the line of resistance of the trunk; thus maximum results in movement are obtained for the force exerted. Since the body is always supported in a balanced position, it may come to rest at any moment, or move forward or backward with equal ease, thus providing a "margin of safety" against any unexpected occurrence or force. The main force used in moving the body forward comes from the muscles of the legs, and since these are large and strong muscles well adapted for this purpose, walking may be continued over long periods of time with relatively little fatigue.

In coordinated sequential walking, the phases described above are not separate occurrences but begin to overlap. The back leg begins its push-off before the front foot strikes the ground, but *not* before the leading leg has been swung through to be ready to receive the body weight. The back leg begins to swing through as the front leg gradually transfers the weight load from the heel, through the outer border of the foot, and on to the front part of the foot preparatory to extending the ankle joint for the next push-off. The trunk does not come to an erect, rigid position between each pair of steps, but remains slightly inclined forward to keep it in line with the extended leg at the time of the push-off, although the inclination is very slight and does not carry the weight center beyond the base of support at any phase of the step. At all times the body is in a balanced state, so that motion can be stopped immediately, a change of direction can be made without losing balance, and there is sufficient factor-of-safety motion to enable the body to absorb any jar or jolt without harm (Figure 20). The weight shift to the alternate feet causes the pelvic girdle to oscillate from front to back, and the arms and shoulders swing slightly to compensate for this oscillation and to keep the body weight evenly distributed; but this oscillating motion and the compensating arm and shoulder swing should be small and relaxed.

Summarizing, the conditions which must be met for maximum efficiency in normal walking are

1. The trunk should be balanced in the pelvic basin, and the head and shoulders should be balanced on the trunk (FPT—MFP).
2. Motion should originate in the hip joint as the leading leg is swung ahead of the body. (Lead with the thigh, not the head.)
3. The leg swing should be straight through and the foot should be set down so that it points straight ahead, ready to receive and transfer the weight in the line of motion. (Apply the force in the direction in which you wish to move.)
4. The trunk should form a continuous straight line with the back leg so that the push-off force will be directed through the weight line and gravity center of the body and all its force will be utilized to move the body diagonally upward-forward over the leading leg. (Apply the force directly through the center of gravity.)
5. The body should make as few extraneous motions as possible, all force being directed in the line of motion. (Be relaxed but don't "fall apart.")

If these conditions are met, the walk will be both efficient and graceful. The strong leg muscles will supply most of the energy for locomotion, and the trunk will float along, being propelled by the legs, without danger of strain to the muscles and joints of the back or impairment of function of the vital organs of the trunk.

An analysis of some of the characteristic modes of walking commonly seen, in terms of these basic conditions, will emphasize the points made and help to focus attention on individual deviations from the efficiently ideal walk. Try each of these as it is described, to feel the effects. One of them may feel so "natural" that you will recognize it as your own.

1. *The Charlie Chaplin Walk.* The toes point outward as the foot is set down, and as the weight is transferred to the front of the foot for the push-off it moves diagonally off its direct course. The push-off is made diagonally from the inside of the foot, and the body is pushed too far in the opposite

direction (Figure 21). Two observable results occur. The path of the walker is a zig to the right followed by a zag to the left, with much energy wasted in diagonal motion. The weight is transferred over the inside of the arch of the foot instead of over the outer border, which is designed for weight bearing. This places a continual strain on the muscles and ligaments

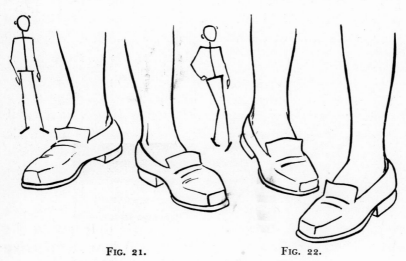

FIG. 21.   FIG. 22.

FIG. 21. The Charlie Chaplin Walker toes out.
FIG. 22. The Cute-Thing Walker toes in.

which support the arch, and the ankle tends to turn inward (*pronate*), while the arch tends to be lowered. The diagonal push-off across the arch tends to exaggerate this effect. The knee joint also may suffer from this continual diagonal push, as it extends diagonally with the weight thrown against the inner ligaments.

2. *The Cute-Thing Walk.* Some girls affect the slightly pigeon-toed walk in the belief that it is "cute" and feminine. The toes point *in* instead of straight ahead as the foot is placed on the ground, and the hip swings in an outcurve to bring the weight around to the diagonal toe-in position (Figure 22). The

push-off is made from the outside of the foot, the joints of the three smallest toes bearing the brunt of the work. The knee joint is twisted, and the upper leg is impeded in its forward swing. The step is short and the swing is not relaxed. More steps must be taken to cover the same distance, and the feet become fatigued because of the unnatural strain on the outside of the foot.

3. *The Rhumba Walk.* This walk (Figure 23) involves an exaggerated shift of the weight to the supporting leg, which causes the hip to move noticeably sideward. To recover the distance lost by sideward motion, the push-off is directed diagonally toward the other side, which in turn throws the weight too far in the opposite direction, and the other hip juts out sideward in its turn. This exaggerated weight shift throws the weight strongly against the ligaments of the hip joint and the side of the knee joint, causing the knee joint to lock momentarily to maintain balance. This

Fig. 23. The pelvis of the Rhumba Walker shifts and oscillates.

walk is usually associated with the slow amble in which the weight rests momentarily on each foot while forward progress is stopped, but it also may occur in rapid walking, creating an effect which corresponds to the football violation of "backfield illegally in motion." Energy is wasted in initiating and stopping the sideward motion, and aesthetically the effect is awkward.

4. *The Eager-Beaver Walk.* This walk (Figure 24) creates an impression of great energy being expended by one who has not a minute to lose. The arms swing stiffly forward and backward in a wide arc, which in turn causes the shoulders to move for-

ward and backward, and the hips must move too far forward and backward to compensate for upper-trunk motion. In efficient walking, the arm swing is natural, relaxed, and unstudied, arising only from the necessity for keeping the body weight centered as the hips swing forward and backward with the movement of the legs. The length of the swing is determined by the length of the stride, and the speed is determind by the speed of the leg stride. The Eager Beaver reverses the sequence of events. He swings his arms so vigorously that he throws his trunk off balance, and the hips must move forward and backward with equal vigor and amplitude to offset the swing of the arms. Since this is not coordinated with the leg swing, the hip is moved too far back for the stride, the leg is twisted slightly, the natural easy swing of the shoulders is inhibited, and force must be used to overcome the resistance offered by

FIG. 24. The Eager-Beaver Walker swings hips, shoulders, and arms in all directions.

the tense muscles. This overcoming of resistance produces an awkward, jerky walk which defeats the purpose of the Beaver, who is trying to get somewhere in a hurry. He produces a great breeze, but he arrives late and is tired out when he gets there. The hip swing and arm swing are so closely related that it is sometimes difficult to tell which is cause and which is effect. An exaggerated arm swing produces exaggerated hip motion, but the converse also is true, and the excess motion may originate in the hip swing and be transferred to the arms.

5. *The Nervous-Nelly Walk.* Nelly is close kin to the Beaver, but where the Beaver swings his arms vigorously in a wide arc, Nelly swings hers from the elbow only. Her upper arms are close to her sides, her shoulders are stiff and tense and slightly hunched, her head protrudes between her stiff shoulders as she

peers at the world with worried eyes. She walks with quick, tense steps, and the very tension keeps her steps shorter than they would be if her legs were allowed to swing normally through in a relaxed manner. As she hurries her stiff legs the hips move back and forth tensely, and her stiff shoulders move to match them. Below her elbows, her arms dangle in an uncontrolled manner and swing back and forth. She uses tremendous energy to move herself about, but most of it is wasted in overcoming the resistances which her tense manner has created, and little energy is actually being utilized to push her body forward.

6. *The Peg-Leg Walk.* Here the weight is carried so far backward that the knee joint is hyperextended or locked to combat the backward pull of gravity. The backward distribution of the body weight throws the center of gravity behind the hip joint, the lower back is hollowed, the pelvic girdle tilted, and the trunk is deprived of support. The knee is practically rigid and no pushing force can be supplied by the extension of the knee joint. The ankles and feet must supply all of the push, and the walk becomes heavy and jerky. As the leading foot strikes the ground, the knee is still stiff and the heel strikes with a jar which is transmitted to the whole body. This walk is fatiguing, not only to the legs and feet, but to the back as well.

7. *The Splash-Kick Walk.* Many walkers complain of splashing mud on the back of their shoes and hose. This is an interesting example of an apparently minor deviation in the walking pattern which produces undesirable results. As the foot pushes off, there is a slight twist on the ball of the foot which moves the heel toward the outside. This quick change of direction causes the drops of mud or dirt which cling to the heel to fly off in the opposite direction, and the other foot which is swinging through becomes a target for them. If carefully observed, this walk will be seen also to produce a slight hip swing, for the whole leg is twisted by the motion of the foot, and the hip is forced out of line.

8. *The Ankle-Kick Walk.* This walk is of the same origin as the Splash-Kick, but the twist is in the opposite direction. As the foot pushes off, the heel is twisted inward. In this position it swings through and kicks the other leg on the protruding ankle bone. The hip swing appears on the side opposite the twisted foot as the push shifts the body weight too far in the opposite direction.

9. *The Upsy-Daisy Walk.* This walk (Figure 25) appears buoyant and exuberant as the body bobs up and down with every step, as if the walker had springs in his shoes. The final

Fig. 25. The head of the Upsy-Daisy Walker rises and falls.

push from the toes is directed more nearly upward than forward, and the body rises with the push and must come down again as the leading foot strikes the floor. The up-and-down motion is wasted energy, since it moves the body at right angles to the line of direction. If a body weighing 150 pounds is raised an unnecessary three inches with each step, it is obvious that a considerable amount of extra work is done which accomplishes nothing.

10. *The Looking-for-Pennies-on-the-Pavement Walk.* This walk (Figure 26) is characterized by the forward head and shoulders. If the body is held stiffly, this walk closely resembles the Nervous-Nelly Walk, and the characteristic head lead, without tension, is also found in walks of the gorilla type. In either case, the pull exerted by gravity on the muscles of the back and neck and the abdominal wall is the same. The center of gravity tends to fall ahead of the hip joint, and each push given by the legs tends to topple the trunk farther forward. The back leg must be brought forward quickly to catch the falling body; much of its pushing force is lost, and additional energy is

required to contract the leg muscles forcibly to resist the for-ward-downward-moving body.

11. *The I-Don't-Care Walk.* This walk is characterized by shuffling feet and a lack of control of body movements. The body is partially collapsed and the arms and head dangle list-lessly, swinging with every motion of the body. Energy is con-

Fig. 26. The Looking-for-Pennies-on-the-Pavement Walker is in danger of falling forward.

sumed by every aimless motion, and the walker becomes more fatigued and listless with every step. The chest is sunken, the abdomen protrudes, and the heart and lungs are crowded. Oxygen is supplied by an occasional involuntary sigh, sufficient to keep the body alive, but the brain functions on half rations and takes less and less interest in its surroundings. Boredom and lassitude increase; the walker is not only unlovely but unloved.

These are some of the most commonly observed energy wasters, but others also will be noted, peculiar to certain individuals. While it may be helpful to recognize the particular fault which is to be overcome, so that specific attention may later be focused on it, it is easier to begin by trying to get the feeling of an efficient walk in its totality. After the general picture is visualized and the feel of it is perceived kinesthetically, details may be corrected as needed.

Begin practice of the easy, efficient walk by a quick check to be sure that the body is balanced in the standing position. Emphasize the necessity for freedom to move in each anatomically possible direction in every joint, so that movement may be accomplished without strain or jerkiness. Particularly, be sure that the trunk is well balanced on the pelvic girdle and that the pelvic girdle is in a balanced position to enable the legs to move freely from the hip joint without strain.

When the balanced position is achieved, place an imaginary bucket of water on the head. Get it firmly balanced, then move about experimentally to be sure it will not fall off. When it is securely balanced, allow the imaginary bucket to hang from an imaginary hook directly overhead just high enough for the top of the head to touch it lightly. Keep the head in contact with the bucket; pull down through the end of the spine as if a long heavy tail were attached. Let this tail pull straight down, but at the same time keep your head in contact with the bucket. This "extended balance" keeps the trunk erect and in position to "float" along while the legs do the walking.

Shift the weight slightly to the left and extend the right leg forward, placing the heel on the ground. Slowly push the body weight forward-upward by extending the left ankle and knee. As the weight moves forward to the right leg, transfer it smoothly and easily from the heel through the outer border of the foot and then to the front of the foot so the toes can begin the next push-off. Stop and check the balance of the body. Bring the left leg through, and as the heel strikes the ground begin the push-off with the right foot. Stop, and check the body balance. Continue this process very slowly; feel each part of the movement; and be continually conscious of the balance of the trunk and pelvic girdle. With each step feel the heel strike first, then the weight transfer along the supporting outer margin of the foot to the ball of the foot, and then feel the final push-off with the toes. Feel the push of the back leg. Is the bucket still balanced? Is the tail still hanging straight down? Then gradually increase the tempo to a steady "push, push, push" in normal walking rhythm, the back leg doing the pushing job and the trunk almost floating along in its freedom from strain and effort.

Stop in good balanced position. Experiment with this feeling of balance by starting a step then stopping it quickly, as if to avoid an obstacle. In the truly balanced walking position, motion can be stopped at any point in the step, for the body is always securely balanced over a supporting base; the body can move forward or backward with equal ease; or the entire body can change direction without loss of stability.

Walk three steps forward, two steps backward, one step forward, three steps backward, two steps forward, without stopping motion or allowing the trunk to move back and forth from its supported position. Walk three steps and turn, two steps and turn, step, turn, step, turn, in the manner of "To the rear—march!" in military parlance. If the body is well balanced and the supporting base is always either under or ahead of the body, the body can make these changes of direction with its erect position undisturbed and with no arm or hip flinging. Do it easily, without tension, thinking always of the bucket above and the tail hanging down.

Now walk past a full-length mirror, or have someone else serve as the mirror which reveals what others see. Observe the minor or major corrections needed to bring the body into easy alignment. It may be "Head up!" or "Shoulders easy!" or "Knees relaxed." Make such corrections easily, moving the part from the incorrect position to the correct position and back again several times to get the feel of both the right and wrong positions, so that the body will be aware of the wrong position whenever habit causes it to occur.

Walk toward the mirror, observing the full-front impression others receive. Watch the arm swing, the hip swing, and the direction of the foot as it swings through and strikes the floor to receive the body weight. Repeat the process described above for any necessary corrections.

To emphasize the feeling of certain parts of the walk, exaggerate them. Stop in the balanced position and swing one leg forward, stopping it just before it strikes the floor. Have a partner observe whether it is moving straight through and whether the foot is pointing straight ahead. Do the motion incorrectly, calling to your partner what you think you are doing—inswing, or outswing; straight swing with foot turned in; straight swing with foot turned out; or straight swing with foot straight. It is surprising to find that the mind often thinks the leg is doing one thing, while observation reveals that it has moved quite differently.

Start with the feet parallel; observe the distance between them. Walk a few steps and come to a quick stop. Note whether the feet are parallel or whether the toes have tended to turn in or out. If the toes are habitually turned out, a "pigeon-toed feeling" will result from the first attempts to get them into a straight line. Practice walking with the toes straight ahead until every stop shows them in the original starting position. Keep the head up, "feel" with the feet.

Stand against the wall with the body easily balanced. Consciously initiate the motion in the hip joint by stepping forward on one foot. Note the feeling of the back leaving the wall as the body slants forward to receive the push from the back foot. Walk straight across the room to the opposite wall. If the leg and thigh are really leading the walk and the body is still balanced, the foot or knee should touch the opposite wall before the body reaches it. If the body strikes the wall ahead of the foot or leg, the trunk is leaning too far forward for a normal walk.

Stand in a balanced position and fold both arms across the chest; hold the shoulders firmly. Walk rapidly in this position, noticing how the hip swing increases when it is not compensated for by the easy swing of the arms.

After these experiments, again return to the easy balanced walk, and observe that the principle of FPT applies just as well in walking as it does in standing. The base is now an *alternating* one, but if the walk is performed in the balanced position the trunk is always directly over the pelvic girdle and the pelvic girdle is always over one of the feet or over the area between them. At all times the body is able to move in any anatomically possible direction, for no joint is strained to its limit and the factor-of-safety motion is always present. In this balanced posture there is always sufficient spring to absorb any jolts or jars arising from walking on an uneven surface or from suddenly stepping up or down without warning, and there is no phase of insecurity when the body is entirely at the mercy of gravity with no support available. All the motions are under easy control, and the work is being done by the strong muscles of the legs, which can continue for long periods without strain.

When the feeling of a dynamically correct walk has been achieved, this feeling can be strengthened by alternating it with poor walking postures, followed by correction to the balanced position. The body may also be put deliberately through a series of movements in which all of the parts are momentarily unbalanced, finishing with a balanced posture and movement from the balanced position. Such exercises help to establish the feeling of the difference between the balanced and the unbalanced position and serve as a stimulus and aid to correction.

For example, in walking down the street the body may gradually slip out of its original position into the gorilla type of walk. Kinesthetic perception should be great enough to make the walker aware that this has occurred, and the desire to prevent such an occurrence should be strong enough to cause him to return to the balanced position without conspicuous effort.

To create this situation for purposes of practice, begin walking in the best balanced position possible. Gradually allow the pelvis to tip so that the end of the spine moves backward and upward and the lower back is hollowed. Without breaking stride, correct this position, bringing the pelvis back to the neutral position of support. Then allow the pelvic girdle to rotate in the opposite direction until the tip of the spine moves under the body and the slumped fatigue posture occurs. Again without breaking stride, correct this position to bring the pelvis back to its point of balance.

Similarly, experiment with other inefficient walks, particularly the one which feels most "comfortable." Make the change from the inefficient walk to the balanced walk and back again a sufficient number of times to establish the feeling of both. The awareness of the feeling of being unbalanced is essential if the bad habit is to be corrected.

Rapid walking also presents certain problems of efficiency and inefficiency. In walking, each leg acts as a pendulum and swings through under the body in an arc. A pendulum of a given length and weight has a normal rate of swing. This rate can be altered by pushing the pendulum so that it moves faster or by holding it back so that it will swing more slowly; but additional energy must be spent to effect these alterations in the normal rate of swing. In trying to walk rapidly, it is not unusual for the walker to tense the muscles of the legs and try to push them more rapidly through their alternating motion. This tension actually shortens the stride, and the walker moves with tense, choppy, and shorter steps. This pace is very fatiguing and results in no increase in speed. Much breeze is created by the jerky movements of the body, giving an illusion of haste, but the objective is reached no sooner, and the walker is more fatigued when he arrives.

The easy way to increase the speed of walking is to lengthen the arc of the swinging leg, allowing it to swing through this lengthened arc at its normal rate. The center of gravity of the body should be lowered by relaxing the knees and allowing them to bend slightly, thus bringing the hips closer to the ground. When this is done, the heel will strike farther from the body, producing a longer stride with no additional expenditure of energy. The back leg will then form a more acute angle with the ground, and more of the diagonal pushing force will be effective in the forward direction. The rapid walk produced by lengthening the stride should be relaxed and easy, and the force applied need be no greater than that used for the normal gait. The modification used to produce more rapid locomotion is in the angle of application of force and in the lowering of the center of gravity. Because of the greater length of the stride, the hips oscillate over a wider arc; this should be compensated for by a longer swing of the arms and shoulders. This will occur naturally if the arms and shoulders are relaxed. This is the walking technique used by the woodsman who travels long distances tirelessly with his long swinging stride, easily swinging arms, and relaxed body.

To experience the principles discussed above, start by standing erect with the knees tense. Extend one leg forward and note the point at which the heel strikes the ground. Then relax the supporting leg, allowing the knee to bend slightly. Note how much farther forward the other leg may be extended with no feeling of strain.

Walk rapidly about the room, consciously pushing the legs to produce the maximum number of steps per minute. Note how tense the body becomes, and how quickly the leg muscles fatigue. This fatigue will be felt most acutely in the large muscle of the back of the leg (the *gastrocnemius*) and may result in acute cramps in the leg if the pace is continued too long.

Now consciously relax the knees. Walk about the room using as long a step as can be taken without forcing the leg forward. Compare the number of steps required to cross the room using the relaxed swinging stride with the number required when the body is held tense and the legs are forced to move rapidly. Compare the time required to cover the same distance using the two methods. Compare the feeling of fatigue resulting from the two methods. The tense rapid walk tends to throw the body forward, out of balance. The "lowered center of gravity" walk makes it easy to maintain the balanced position of the trunk while the arms, shoulders, and hips move easily as they adjust to the lengthened stride.

A somewhat different problem of locomotion is encountered by girls who wear high-heeled slippers. Many girls who move easily and freely in their saddle shoes suddenly become awkward and stilted when they "dress up." The heel is raised three or more inches and the foot is tilted forward. To maintain balance on this forward-sloping foot, the walker tends to lock her knees and throw her hips backward, hollowing the lower back (Fig-

FIG. 27. High heels throw the body forward and the knees are locked to maintain balance.

ure 27). As she begins to walk, the high heel strikes the ground in front sooner than the normal heel would, and the unexpectedness of the contact causes it to strike the ground more forcibly. The high arch of the shoe raises the middle part of the foot so that the outer border of the foot is not in contact with the ground to transfer the weight, resulting in an interval between the time when the heel first receives the weight and the time when the weight is safely transferred to the ball of the foot. During this time the only support available is that derived from the small surface of the heel (about one square inch), instead of the four or five square inches of the heel of the bare foot or the sport shoe. Consequently, the foot wobbles slightly, trying to maintain its balance on this small base. This wobble is increased if the heel strikes ever so slightly off center or on one of the side edges. This wobble gives a feeling of insecurity, the muscles of the leg tighten protectively, the knees tend to lock, and the whole body is thrown farther out of balance as the hips move back and the upper trunk moves forward to compensate for the shift in the base of support.

Standing and walking gracefully in high heels is possible if the posture and movement are adapted to the sloping, insecure base. The adjustment to the changed foot position should be made with the entire body as a unit, rather than by zigging the legs and hips backward and zagging the abdomen forward. The knees should be kept relaxed, the pelvis pulled down into the natural, supporting position, the trunk and head well balanced, and the entire body, *in a straight line,* moved slightly backward from the *ankles* to achieve balance in the new position. This will slightly alter the position of the center of gravity with relation to the feet, moving it a bit more toward the heels; but this is of minor consequence when compared with the strains induced by the zigzag adjustments.

This balance can be maintained in walking by shortening the step. The shorter step reduces the angle at which the wobbly heel strikes the ground, allowing the entire heel to receive the weight and to transfer it more quickly to the ball of the foot, thus decreasing the period of insecurity. During each step the weight rests on the entire foot for a greater period of time. Shortening the step without increasing the rate of movement obviously reduces the speed of walking, but this is unimportant, since high heels are designed for moments of leisure.

Walking in high heels requires more conscious control than walking in low-heeled shoes, for it is not a normal type of locomotion. However, the walk should not be stilted, mincing, or ambling. It should be easy, relaxed, and leisurely. The more rapid such a walk becomes the more difficult it is to maintain the relaxed balanced posture. This leads to the observation that women who are in a hurry should wear low-heeled shoes!

For achieving balance, ease, and efficiency in all types of walking, the important thing is practice—practice carried on until the balanced position becomes the natural and comfortable position. This practice should be varied, but it must be persistent. Formal practice may be carried on for short periods over many days, but the most effective practice is that which is a part of every day's activities. Observing poor posture in a friend or passer-by should serve as a reminder to check FPT. Appearing before a group in the classroom, at an assembly, or at a club meeting should be a challenge to walk to that featured spot with balanced ease, arriving there with composure and self-confidence. Reminder points should be set up at various locations during the day. Walking out the door to start the day is a cue to get balanced, move easily, and start the day right. Every door may serve as a check point to pass through with minimum motion and maximum balance. Glancing in a plate glass window, which everyone does either consciously or unconsciously, gives an image of the balanced or unbalanced posture and should create an urge to correct any deficiencies.

These devices sound very simple. They will be effective only to the extent that they are motivated by a real desire to improve, to find the ease of movement which comes from the balanced posture in motion.

PROJECTS FOR FURTHER STUDY

1. Working with a partner, critically watch each other walk. Note any peculiarities which keep the walk from being smooth and attractive. Determine which of the principles for efficient walking are being ignored. Make suggestions for improvement.

2. At the next opportunity, observe the postures of people dancing. Mentally list the awkward postures you observe for the girls. Do the same for the men. Try those postures in front of a full-length mirror. What principles are being ignored? How can the awkward postures be made graceful? Assume each awkward posture as you dance with a partner. Apply your own suggestions and change each awkward posture into a balanced FPT posture as you dance.

3. *a.* Make your body as stiff and tense as possible. Walk rapidly around the room, noting the feeling of restriction. Listen to the sound made by your heels as you walk.

   b. Relax, and in good balanced FPT posture, walk rapidly around the room, noting the difference in feeling. Again listen to the sound your heels make as you walk.

   What accounts for the difference in sound?

4. Try each of the walks described in this chapter. Without stopping, correct each one to the balanced FPT walk.

5. For one day consciously observe people walking. Write a paper on "Walks I Have Seen."

9

The Balanced Posture: Working

THE LIVING body is constantly transforming energy. The food which is eaten and the air which is breathed are the sources of the energy which is transformed and expended by the body for maintenance and movement. When the energy outgo exceeds the energy income, fatigue results and the individual "feels tired" and is unwilling to continue work until such time as the deficit has been repaid. If he forces himself to continue working while fatigued, he works with decreased efficiency, spending more and more energy to produce less and less results. If he works constantly in a state of partial fatigue, he becomes increasingly inefficient, eventually reaching a state in which he is producing minimum results with maximum effort.

The energy reserves of the healthy body are very great, but they are not limitless. Every useless motion, every unnecessary muscle contraction, every needless force exerted to combat the pull of gravity takes its toll of the body energy and decreases the total amount of useful work or pleasurable play which the body may perform in a given time. Every useless motion eliminated, every needless muscle contraction saved increases the energy reserves of the body and makes it possible for the body to work or play longer with greater efficiency and less fatigue. No intelligent person begrudges the free expenditure of energy to accomplish a given purpose. But motion which accomplishes nothing is wasteful, and no intelligent person would willingly fritter away his energy in awkward, strained, or unnecessary movements which bring him no pleasure or useful results and serve only to increase his fatigue and decrease his enjoyment of living. It follows, then, that the intelligent, physically educated individual has learned to streamline his movements, eliminating from them all possible sources of wasted energy. His reward is not only efficiency but ease and grace of motion, which illustrates the quotation from Plato used to begin this book: "The most beautiful motion is that which accomplishes the greatest results with the least amount of effort."

Every movement which the body makes in work or play is different from every other movement, but certain energy-saving principles are applicable to all movement. If these principles are understood and *applied* to all activities in which the body engages, much energy may be saved and much fatigue averted. Most of these principles have been presented either directly or indirectly in the preceding chapters. They are summarized here for application to other activities.

1. When all parts of the body are balanced, the force of gravity pulls the body together. When any part of the body is out of line, the force of gravity pulls that part toward the earth, and force must be exerted by the muscles to hold the body together.
   a. Balance is maintained by keeping the center of gravity of any part over its immediate base of support and by keeping the center of gravity of the whole body over the supporting base. (Keep the feet under the pelvis and the pelvis under the trunk.)
   b. Balance is maintained most easily when each body part is *centered* over its base.
   c. If the balance of the body is threatened by some external force, balance can be more easily maintained if the base of support is increased in size. (Spread the base for greater stability.)
   d. Balance is maintained more easily if all parts of the body are kept close to the line of gravity and not allowed to extend

beyond the base or to zigzag back and forth above it. (Remember the Christmas tree.)

2. External weights added to the body become part of the total body weight and affect the location of the center of gravity, displacing it in the direction of the added weight. The effect of such weights increases with their distance from the center of gravity. (Effective force equals weight times distance.)

   a. Keep additional weights close to the body and as nearly as possible over the base of support.

   b. Adjust the position of the total body-plus-weight *as a unit*, to keep the new center of gravity over the base without throwing some part of the body out of line to counterbalance the added weight.

3. To move the body or any external object, force must be applied. This force is most effective if it is applied directly through the center of gravity in the direction in which movement is desired.

   a. Force applied above, below, or on either side of the center of gravity causes the body or object to rotate about its center of gravity as it moves diagonally away from the direction of the force. (Don't push on a corner.)

   b. If the weight to be moved is not in line with the moving force, the rotatory and diagonal motions set up must be combated with the application of additional force supplied by resisting muscles. (Every zig must have its zag.)

4. When the body is in motion, balance is maintained more easily if a new base of support is always prepared before the center of gravity is allowed to move from its original base. (Lead with the thigh, not with the head.)

5. The center of gravity of the body is approximately at the level of the hip joint. All large movements of the trunk and legs should originate at or pass through this point. (Move from the hip joint, not from the waistline.)

6. Strong muscles perform a task more efficiently than weak or small muscles. For any given task, the strongest muscles available should be used. (Walk with the legs, not with the back.)

7. The movement of any part about a joint is limited by the ligaments which hold the joint together.

a. A joint forced to its extreme range of motion is in a position of potential injury. Every joint should have freedom to "give" in any held position. (The factor-of-safety motion.)

b. Sudden or uncontrolled shifts of weight throw the weight of the part against the ligaments, stretching and weakening them. When a joint is to be subjected to a sudden shift in motion, it should be prepared for it and protected by the controlled use of the opposing muscles. (Never throw the weight against a joint.)

FIG. 28. She "pulls on a corner" and strains her back.

These principles can be applied or defied in any of the simple actions of daily living. Take, for example, the commonplace act of picking a flower which grows close to the ground. This can be a back-straining or a back-strengthening process. It all depends on how it is done. Figure 28 shows a woman wasting energy and in danger of straining her back as she works in her garden. Figure 29 shows her performing the same task in complete safety and with minimum expenditure of effort.

How did she approach her task in the first picture? With feet together she started to bend from the waist. As she started to lose balance, her hips moved backward to balance the forward weight of her bent body. As she reached forward to grasp the flower she stretched every joint in her back and in her shoulder to its full range of motion, and in this insecure position she locked her knees to give herself a feeling of support.

Her head is forward, dangling from her neck, and the entire weight of her trunk is supported by the muscles and ligaments which cross the hip joint in back. Any slight jar or push will send her sprawling, for she has reached her limit of compensation and she has no factor-of-safety motion left to absorb any sudden force, however slight.

To rise to the erect position, either with or without the flower, she must depend on a strong contraction of the gluteal

FIG. 29. She maintains FPT, applies force through the center of gravity, and works in safety.

muscles with an assist from the extensor muscles of the back. The gluteal muscles are "pulling on a corner" to try to raise a heavy, tottering weight against the pull of gravity. In this insecure situation any sudden jerk may easily throw uncontrolled weight against the joints of the back or the important joints which connect the spinal column with the pelvic girdle (the lumbosacral and sacroiliac joints), forcing them beyond their anatomical limits of motion.

"Oh, my aching back" becomes more than an expression, it becomes a reality for this poor unbalanced creature. In addition, she has the doubtful satisfaction of knowing that she has made an unaesthetic spectacle of herself in this ungainly position.

What principles did she fail to apply? First, she knew she

was going to lower and raise her own weight in addition to the
weight of the flower, which was negligible. She was going to
disturb her own balance and become unstable. The first principle she should have applied was: "If the balance of the body
is threatened, balance can be more easily maintained if the
base of support is increased in size." She should have spread
her base for greater stability by separating her feet and putting
one of them slightly ahead of the other, giving her stability
sideward as well as forward and backward. Then, remembering that balance is maintained by keeping the weight centered
over the base, she should have moved closer to the flower to
prevent reaching out and bringing her body beyond the base
of support, thus necessitating a Christmas-tree kind of balance
with the hips forming the opposing branches. Then, still determined to keep the center of gravity over the supporting base,
and remembering that all major movements originate in the
hip joint, she should have begun her crouch by allowing the
hip, knee, and ankle joints to flex, lowering her weight over
the supporting base and controlling the lowering with the
strong extensor muscles of the back of the hip joint, the front
of the thigh, and the back of the calf, thus keeping her feet
under her pelvis and her pelvis under her trunk (and inci-
dentally, her hips lower than her head). In this position she
could lower her body only until her hand reached the ground
or the flower without strain or reaching. Every part of the body
would be directly over the supporting base, and no part would
be moved to the limit of its anatomical range of motion. In
this position she could move her body forward, backward, or
to either side without upsetting her balance or throwing her
weight suddenly against a joint without sufficient "give" to
absorb the shock. She could pick the flower easily, without
strain, and without fear. As she started to rise, no "pulling on
a corner" problem would present itself. The strong extensor
muscles of the leg and thigh, assisted by the gluteal muscles,
would contract to extend the ankle, knee, and hip joints to

push the body back to an erect position. Since the body weight
would be directly above the pushing force, none of the force
would be wasted, and the body would rise to the erect position
with a minimum amount of effort, using three sets of strong
muscles. The gentle curve of the back would be straightened
by the extensor muscles of the back without strain or jerk.
The strong muscles of the leg, working through the line of
gravity, would perform with ease and safety what the weaker
muscles of the back, working at a disadvantage with their corner pull, performed with danger and difficulty. Aesthetically,
the difference is obvious. As she went down, she would have
taken her hips down with her and kept them tucked down
under her body, where they belong, instead of thrusting them
upward and backward toward the sky or the gaze of the dis-
gusted observer.

Try these two methods of lowering and raising the body
weight and feel the difference when the principles are first
defied and then applied. If no flower is available, a dropped
handkerchief will do just as well. Stand back away from it with
the feet together. Reach forward and downward toward the
handkerchief and feel the strain on the back, hip joints, and
back of the legs. Move suddenly in this position, imagining
that the handkerchief is a buzzing bee. Straighten up and feel
the pull on the muscles of the back and the gluteal muscles.
Notice the tendency to straighten too far and overbalance backward with the back hollowed. The strong sharp pull—almost
a jerk—required to lift the body by pulling on the lower edge
is difficult to control, and the momentum imparted to the body
after its resistance is overcome tends to carry the body backward beyond the normal point of rest or balance.

In good balanced position, repeat the act of picking up the
handkerchief easily and with minimum strain. Standing close
to the object with the feet slightly spread, sink easily downward
using the ankle, knee, and hip joints and distributing the
work to be done over the muscles which cross the three sets of

joints. With the trunk bent easily forward in a slight curve
to keep the weight centered over the spread base and to bring
the shoulder girdle over the object to be lifted, reach down
with the nearest hand and pick up the handkerchief. Then
rise easily by extending the three sets of joints, ankle, knee and
hip, their combined action pushing the body upward while
the slightly curved back straightens without strain. Two cau-
tions: Do not go down farther than is necessary to reach the
handkerchief easily, and keep the knee nearest the object out of
the way by stepping back on that foot and forward on the foot
farthest away from the object to be retrieved. Try it again,
consciously observing that the principle of FPT is never violated
and noting how easy it is to move forward, backward, up, or
down without upsetting the balance of the body.

This same motion pattern is applicable in all acts in which
the body weight is lowered and in which work is done on the
ground level. Working in the garden, picking strawberries,
dusting the lower rungs of the furniture—in all these activities
and many others the body weight is either lowered momentarily or lowered and held in the squat position for an extended
period of time. If the position is to be held for minutes, the
body may be moved about by reversing the relationship of the
two legs.

If the job to be done is a long one and the hands must be
kept at ground level for some time, it will be easier to create a
larger and more secure base by kneeling, using the entire lower
leg for support. The change of position from squatting to kneeling can be made without raising the body weight more than a
few inches, and the change of position from time to time delays
the onset of fatigue and prevents cramps in the bent knees. If
the body is to be held in the full-squat position, additional
support for the trunk may be secured by sitting on the heel of
the bent foot. This is a comfortable position and places no
particular strain on the bent foot, for the bulk of the body

weight is borne by the other leg with its foot firmly planted on the ground.

The use of the quarter, half, or three-quarter squat in preference to the full waistline stoop is important when a light object is to be retrieved from the ground; it becomes increasingly important when the object to be lifted has weight of its own which must be added to the body weight. "External weights added to the body become part of the total body weight and affect the location of the center of gravity, displacing it in the direction of the added weight. The effect of such weights increases with their distance from the center of gravity."

The weight to be lifted, which, of course, is acted upon by gravity, must be considered as a downward force to be overcome. This force is not the weight of the object alone, but the weight of the object multiplied by the horizontal distance from the joint around which the lifting arms or body must be rotated. This principle is illustrated simply by the childhood experience of balancing a seesaw. A large child sitting close to the sawhorse or balance point can be balanced or lifted by a smaller child sitting farther away from the point of support. The closer the object is to the lifting force, the smaller will be the downward resistance to be overcome and the less will be the energy or muscle contraction required to lift it.

To lift a heavy object, whether it be a sack of potatoes or a small child, the principles to be applied are the same. Get close to the object. Spread the base to increase the stability of the body. Lower the body weight through the line of gravity by bending the hip, knee, and ankle joints. When the body is lowered until the arms can easily control the object to be lifted, either at the side or between the bent knees in front, get a firm grasp on the object or put the arms under or around it. Remembering that the closer the weight is to the line of gravity the easier it will be to lift it, bring the object up and in toward the body *before* beginning to extend the ankle, knee and hip joints to raise the body to the erect position. A common fault

in lifting is in extending the ankles, knees, and hip joints before
the object is brought in to the body. This brings the hips up
into the air above the head, and the problems of the woman
trying to raise her body weight after picking a flower in the
waistline-stoop position are greatly exaggerated by the additional weight of the object to be lifted (Figure 30). With the

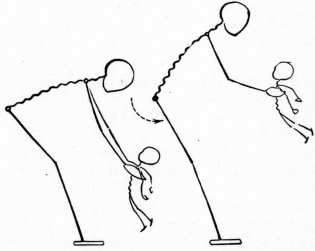

FIG. 30. The weight of the baby hangs on her arms and back.

sack of potatoes held close to the body or the baby held against
one shoulder, the entire weight of the body-plus-object may
be easily pushed into the erect position by the strong extension
of the three pairs of leg joints, without danger of strain or pull
on the shoulder joint, the back, or the lumbosacral joint
(Figure 31).

In the erect position with the potatoes or baby held against
the front of the body, a new problem presents itself, that of
adjusting to the new position of the center of gravity, which
has been moved forward by the added weight in front. The
tendency is to offset this forward zig by a backward zag of the
shoulders and upper body. If this is not sufficient, the hips may

also be thrown backward to move additional weight backward
to balance the weight in front, the knee joints being locked for
support. These two adjustments force the lower back to hollow
in an exaggerated curve, and the joints of the back are forced
to their anatomical limit of movement. If the potatoes slip or

FIG. 31. The weight of the baby is held close to the center of gravity,
directly above the pushing force.

the baby makes a sudden motion, the back has no factor-of-
safety motion left to adjust to the sudden change of position,
and damage or strain may readily result. In this zigzag, strained
position, walking becomes a dangerous activity. The pelvic
girdle is not aligned with the legs, the lower back is hollowed
to its limit, and the upper back is overhanging the whole
structure. Each step becomes a jolt and a jar, the force of which
is transmitted to the entire spinal column, being felt most
keenly at the point where the spine joins the sacrum. This is
not only a fatigue-inducing position but a potentially dangerous
one (Figure 32).

The FPT principle still applies, even though additional weight has been added to the body. "Adjust the position of the total body-plus-weight as a unit, keeping the new center of

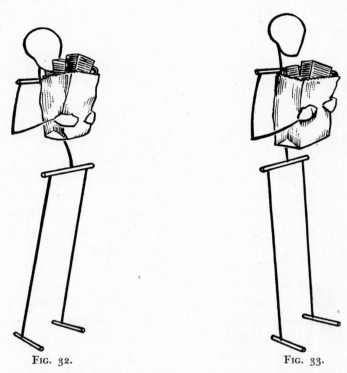

Fig. 32.   Fig. 33.

Fig. 32. The back is hollowed, the trunk tilted backward, and the knees locked as the weight is supported on the abdomen.

Fig. 33. FPT is maintained by adjusting the total body-plus-weight as a unit, starting at the base.

gravity over the base without throwing any part of the body out of line to counterbalance the added weight." This can be done easily by starting the adjustment at the base. Keeping the trunk and pelvis in their balanced alignment, consciously let the weight of the entire body shift backward toward the heels by adjusting the relationship of the lower leg to the foot.

Actually there is little or no shift in the position of the line of gravity with relation to the feet, for the added weight has moved the gravital line forward. The shift merely brings it back to the balanced position. Because the angle of the lower leg with the foot has been slightly altered, there is kinesthetic awareness of the shift, which seems exaggerated because it is "different" from the normal balance relationship (Figure 33).

In this adjusted-from-the-base position there is no strain on the joints of the back, the pelvic girdle is in its normal position, and the jar of walking is absorbed by the factor-of-safety motion which is still present. The aching-back fatigue is avoided, and the weight may be carried easily for a longer distance without awareness of pain in overstrained joints.

The potatoes or the baby should be kept as close as possible to the center of gravity to reduce the rotational force set up by the downward pull of gravity. Ideally, the weight should be carried directly over the supporting base. Oriental women accomplish this by carrying all weights on their heads, the downward force being resisted by the entire body structure. This procedure is a little dangerous for those who have not trained in it from youth, for it requires very strong neck muscles and a very sure sense of balance to keep the head and the weight in the exactly erect position. The waitress who carries a heavy tray on one shoulder makes a different type of adjustment. She has added weight to one side of her body. To compensate for it, she leans to the opposite side to balance the tray and keep the gravity line of body-plus-tray centered over her base. The inexperienced waitress does it by adjusting from her waistline, and she soon learns that this is a most fatiguing process.

This same principle can be applied to carrying a weight, such as a pail or a suitcase, by a handle, the weight being supported entirely by one arm and hand. The one-arm lift should still be an ankle-knee-hip-joint lift, the body being lowered until the hand can easily grasp the handle, then the pail or suitcase and the body lifted to the erect position by the extension of

the ankle-knee-hip-joint trio. (Figures 34 and 35). If the
suitcase is carried close to the body, its downward rotational
force is reduced to a minimum because the horizontal distance
from the handle to the gravital line of the body is very small,

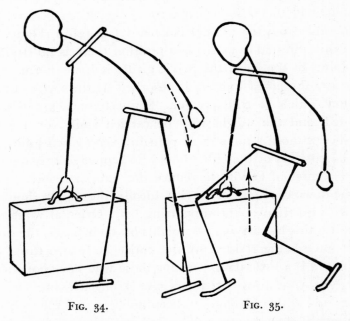

FIG. 34.   FIG. 35.

FIG. 34. The twisted-back lift is done with the small back muscles in a
position of potential strain.
FIG. 35. The ankle-knee-hip-joint lift utilizes the strong muscles of the
legs.

but the added weight still moves the center of gravity toward
the side on which the suitcase is carried. To balance this force,
the weight of the body must be shifted to the opposite side. If
this is done from the waistline, the spine is curved and the
joints are forced out of line (Figure 36). Again the answer is to
shift from the base, slanting the whole body slightly sideward
to balance the weight of the suitcase on the opposite side
(Figure 37). Ideally, the problem is best solved by carrying *two*

suitcases, one on each side for balance, but this is not always practicable. If the suitcase is very heavy, or if the pail must be held away from the side of the body to prevent splashing, addi-

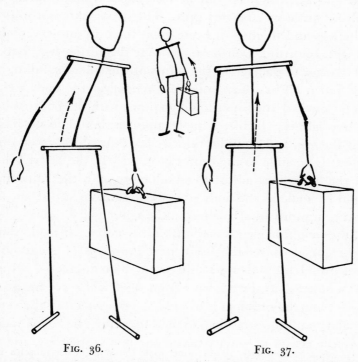

Fig. 36.   Fig. 37.

Fig. 36. Compensating for added weight by shifting the upper trunk puts strain on the back muscles.

Fig. 37. A slight shift starting from the base will balance a heavy suitcase without strain.

tional balance weight on the opposite side may be created by raising the opposite arm sideward. The extended arm, with its weight farther from the line of gravity, becomes a greater balancing force than the same arm held down at the side.

The three-joint principle applies in many other situations when the body weight must be lowered and then raised against a resisting force. Opening a heavy window or lifting a car bumper to free it from an entanglement with another automobile bumper are good examples. The arms, shoulder girdle, and curved back are not good tools for exerting a strong lifting force, and when they operate at a mechanical disadvantage the resulting strain may be very great. The strong extensor muscles of the legs and thighs can exert great force in an upward lift, and with the trunk well balanced over the lifting legs there is little danger of damage to the joints of the spinal column.

To put it all in a few sentences: Whenever the body weight is to be lowered, the hips should go down with the body. Whenever a weight is to be lifted, the leg muscles should do the lifting while the arm and shoulder muscles hold the object to be lifted as close as possible to the center of gravity of the body. Whenever the body must adjust to an added weight, the adjustment should be made by the body as a whole, starting at the base and working upward in a balanced although slightly slanting line.

If the weight being carried must ultimately be lifted to shoulder height or above the head, new problems of maintaining balance and minimizing strain present themselves. Lifting a box or suitcase to store it on a high shelf will serve for an example. Now the problem is to raise the weight above the center of gravity with the arms forward and upward. The added weight above the center of gravity makes the body top-heavy, and the potential rotating force of the weight increases with each inch it is raised.

The woman who strained her back picking a flower might perform the task in this manner. She places a chair almost directly under the shelf. Then she climbs on the chair and bends down from the waist to pull the suitcase up to her. Standing facing the shelf with both feet together, she lifts the suitcase in both arms, bending backward at the waist to balance it. Her knees are locked at the extreme backward position. As the suitcase passes her shoulders she bends her head back to get it out of the way, thus increasing the backward curve of her spine and neck, forcing every joint to its limit of motion. In this dangerous and potentially unbalanced position she gets the suitcase above her head, hoping that the momentum of the lift will not carry it too far back. At this point she is really in a dangerous position (Figure 38). If she misjudges the ability of her arms to control the moving weight of the suitcase and lets it move ever so slightly too far back over her head, she will over-balance backward, for the entire weight of her upper trunk and shoulder girdle is directed backward and she cannot support additional force in that direction. Even if she succeeds in catching herself before she falls, the rapid shift of weight backward against joints already strained to their limit of motion is likely to produce strain and pain. If she finally gets the suitcase up to the level of the shelf, she must still push it onto the shelf, bringing her head, arms, and shoulders forward from their insecure position to apply the pushing force. This she does by a sudden shove forward from the waist, throwing her weight line forward toward her toes and forcing her hips backward above her rigid legs. She catches her weight on the edge of the shelf as she gives the case a final shove.

If, later, she wishes to get the suitcase down, she reverses the entire process. She climbs up on the chair directly under the edge of the shelf. Bending backward from the waist with her lower back hollowed, her hips back, her knees locked, and her weight far back on her heels, she reaches up with her hands to grasp the handle of the suitcase. Forgetting that her weight is already back as far as it can safely go, she tugs on the handle, imparting momentum to the suitcase which carries it out and over her head. The rotating force of the suitcase is very great at that distance from the point of support, and it carries her over backward. Standing on the chair she has no room to move her feet backward to provide a new base of support, her back can curve no further to absorb the force, her knees are locked in the backward position, and over she goes, chair, suitcase and all, because she tried to defy the principles of gravity and balance.

Had she analyzed the problem, she would have realized first

that she was about to place her body in a potentially unstable position and she would have "spread the base for greater stability," putting one foot forward and one backward to give her

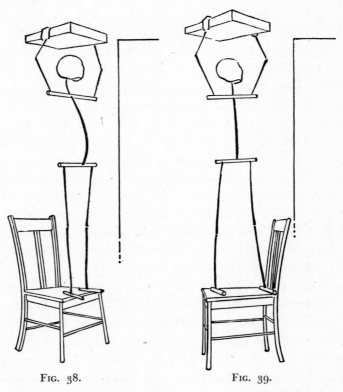

FIG. 38.   FIG. 39.

FIG. 38. Potential danger and strain: feet together, knees locked, trunk bent backward at waist, arms and box behind head.

FIG. 39. FPT and safety: feet astride, knees relaxed, back straight, weight shifted from the base.

a longer base in the forward-backward direction. Maintaining FPT, she would have taken her hips down with her as she reached for the suitcase, shifting her body weight to the back foot to compensate for the weight she was lifting in front. As she raised the case up to waist level she would have adjusted the total body-plus-weight as a unit, keeping all body segments in the position of safety by adjusting her balance from the base of support. As the weight was raised past her center of gravity and upward, she would have let her weight gradually settle on her back foot, keeping her hips well under her trunk and her back reasonably straight to maintain FPT (Figure 39). Should the bag start to topple backward at the top of her reach, she could easily shift her weight to the front foot without moving her feet. In pushing the suitcase onto the shelf, she would remember to "move from the hip joint, not from the waistline," moving her whole trunk forward from the hips to supply the necessary push, supporting her weight easily on the forward foot. Then, bringing her trunk back to its balanced position, with the weight centered between both feet, she could get down from the chair without danger.

To get the suitcase down, the same principles apply. Standing comfortably close to the shelf so that she can reach it easily with her arms, but not so close that her body is almost under the shelf, she stands with her base spread. As her arms are raised forward, her weight shifts easily to the back foot while she maintains FPT. Shifting her balanced body forward to the front foot she grasps the bag and as she pulls it out, shifts her weight back to the rear foot, adjusting the total of body-plus-weight as a unit, making the adjustment from the ankles without shifting her feet. In this easily balanced position she lowers the suitcase, and as it passes the center of gravity she sinks through her hip joints and lowers the suitcase to the floor. At no time has her balance been seriously threatened, and at no time have the joints of her back been forced out of their safe range of alignment. A potentially dangerous task has been made safe and easy.

The same principles apply in many common arm-raising motions more frequently performed. Combing the hair, hanging up laundry, buttoning a dress up the back, driving a nail to hang a picture, reaching for a book on a high shelf, washing or painting walls and ceilings, putting curtains up, brushing cobwebs down—in each of these the arms are raised forward and upward, shifting the center of gravity forward. In the physically uneducated person, there is a tendency to compensate for this forward shift by throwing the upper part of the body backward, hollowing the back, which in turn throws the abdomen forward, which in turn throws the hips backward, which again, in turn, tends to lock the knees in the backward position to keep the weight line from passing the heels. This is a position of potential strain, for the joints of the back and the knee joints are at their limit of safe motion, and any sudden movement, jar, or jolt may force them beyond their limit.

In each instance, the danger of strain may be removed by keeping the body in a balanced position with FPT, by spreading the feet slightly forward and backward and shifting the weight forward and backward from the ankles. In this easy balanced position, the arms and shoulder girdle are free to move in any direction, and the body may adjust easily to the requirements of the movement by shifting over the feet.

Experiment with some of these motions to get the kinesthetic perception of doing them in balance and out of balance. Drive an imaginary nail into the wall. First stand with both feet together close to the wall. Bending backward from the waist to get the face out of range of the hammer, hold the nail with one hand and strike at it with the other. Note the feeling of strain in the curve of the back, and note the small range of movement possible for the arm holding the hammer. Imagine missing the nail, hitting the thumb, and dropping the hammer, and feel what happens as the body tries to adjust to this sudden emergency. Then step back from the wall, standing in stride position with the weight resting easily on the back foot and the body in good FPT alignment. Reach forward with the arms and again drive the nail, noting the difference in arm and shoulder movement, and noting how easy it is to shift the weight to the forward foot as the arm swings the hammer forward and the trunk moves easily at the hip joints.

Lightly massage the scalp with the fingers, or run a brush or comb over the back hair. Note the tendency to adjust from the

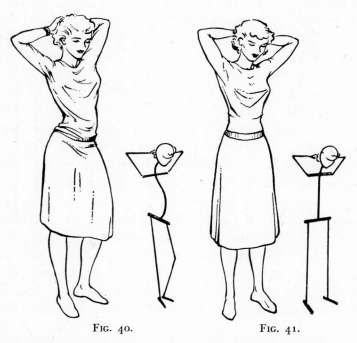

Fig. 40.   Fig. 41.

Fig. 40. Even combing the hair can be a dangerous process with a twisted back.

Fig. 41. Shift from the base to maintain FPT when arms are raised.

waistline instead of from the ankles and the hip joint. Note whether the abdomen tends to protrude and the knees tend to lock as the weight settles backward (Figure 40). Now consciously hold the pelvic girdle where it belongs to maintain FPT, and note how much less tiring the arms-overhead position becomes (Figure 41). Mentally list the principles applied and the principles violated in each instance.

Pushing and pulling are a part of many daily activities. Because additional weight requiring the expenditure of additional force is involved in such tasks, it becomes especially important that the body be protected from the strains associated with poor body mechanics. Pulling out a drawer which tends to stick may be a situation fraught with danger for the

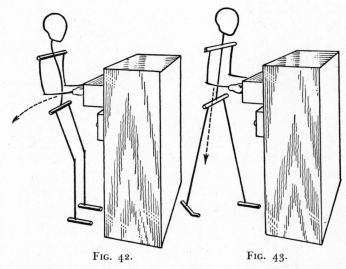

FIG. 42.   FIG. 43.

FIG. 42. A narrow base leaves no room for adjusting to a rapidly shifting weight. The back must take the blow.

FIG. 43. Weight may be shifted over a wide base without destroying FPT.

awkward person. Standing with her feet together, she grasps the handles of the drawer and begins to tug. The drawer refuses to budge. She moves closer to the drawer and jerks mightily, using a quick flexion of her elbows. The drawer gives suddenly, and the momentum of the jerk carries her body backward from the waist, causing a sharp "crick" in her lower back. Or possibly the drawer comes entirely out of its track, almost knocking her down with its weight and force, and she must bend her aching back once more to pick up the spilled contents (Figure 42).

A brief review of the principles of body mechanics would have avoided this catastrophe. First, she should have spread her base for greater stability. With her feet in stride position, she could move her weight back and forth over her base without endangering FPT, and she could easily step backward to maintain her balance if necessary. A slight flexion of her knees and hip joints would give her added range of motion, and she could use the strong muscles of her legs to supply the force of the pull. Her upper body could move easily from the hip joint as she leans toward the drawer to begin her pull and backs away from it as she tugs. No joint would be forced to its extreme range of motion, and she would have sufficient give at every joint to take up any sudden jerk if the drawer gives suddenly. She could even recover in time to reverse the direction of her motion to keep the drawer from coming entirely out of its track (Figure 43).

A simple experiment in hand wrestling will demonstrate the difference in strength of pull in the two positions. Stand facing someone of about your size and strength, clasping hands. Have one person assume the awkward position, feet together, knees straight, and using only the arms and upper body for the pull. Let the other person assume the stride position, with knees and hips slightly flexed. Now try to pull each other off base. Reverse the positions and try it again. The greater stability, safety, and force of the wide-based position with flexed knees and hips becomes very evident (Figure 44).

In pushing, the situation is similar, but the direction of the force is reversed. Maximum pushing force comes from the strong leg and hip muscles, not from the arms and back. Try the hand wrestling experiment again, pushing instead of pulling. Note the greater freedom of movement, the ability to step forward as the weight moves, and the ease of adjusting the height of the push when the strong leg muscles are used (Figure 44).

It would be impossible in this brief book to analyze every possible task that the human body at some time performs. The illustrations given cover the typical situations of activities in which the body weight is lowered and raised; additional weight is lifted, carried, or raised above the center of gravity; weight is moved toward or away from the body. A few additional general suggestions concerning activities done in the standing posi-

Fɪɢ. 44. Greater force may be exerted when pushing and pulling are done over a wide base.

tion may also be helpful in determining the easiest way to do any particular piece of work.

The first principle comes from the lazy man's motto: "Never run when you can walk; never walk when you can stand; never stand when you can sit; and never sit when you can lie." Many stationary tasks, such as ironing, can be done just as well in a sitting position. The housewife who never sits down from morning to night will be a tired person; and the factory worker or the clerk behind the counter who must remain standing in a limited space all day will find that the total fatigue resulting from the day's work will be greatly reduced by occasional sitting.

The second principle is to keep the body balanced—FPT.

Spread the base, or keep moving over a spread base to maintain the balanced position. In this balanced position make the major movements necessary to the task from the hip joint. A bent back becomes a very tired back and may become an aching back. If the body must be inclined forward, as it is in many tasks such as shoveling or sweeping, straighten up from time to time. The change of position will be restful and will delay the onset of fatigue.

The third principle is to keep the work to be done close to you. The body is less effective as a tool when the joints are stretched to their extreme range of motion, and the strain of reaching "just a little bit farther" tends to upset the body balance. Move with your work, and work comfortably and safely.

The most welcome of all military orders, "Take five," is based on sound principles of getting the most work done with the least amount of fatigue. Brief periods of rest will greatly increase the efficiency of the worker in any long-continued task. Change position, stand up and stretch, sit down with the feet raised, stop and chat a minute—and go back to the job with renewed energy. Any task requiring intense concentration, precise movements, or a maximum expenditure of energy will be done better and more quickly if it is not continued to the point of fatigue. How long or how often these rest periods should be will be determined by the nature of the task, but there are few jobs at which the individual may profitably work longer than an hour without a few minutes of rest or diversion.

And finally, set a pace for the job which can be maintained throughout the working period. Rushing at a task in an attempt to do an hour's work in twenty minutes is the surest way to waste both energy and time. The tense, hurried person becomes awkward, he loses the rhythm of his work, and mistakes and fatigue both increase. "Easy does it" is as good a motto for work as it is for exercise.

Deliberate application of the principles discussed in this chapter is the surest way to make the practice of them habitual. Take a number of daily activities and visualize the performance of them. Then actually go through the motions, first doing it awkwardly and in defiance of the principles of efficient body mechanics; then doing it as efficiently and safely as possible.

Or take your favorite sport—tennis, golf, badminton, archery, bowling, or whatever it may be. Watch the skilled performer and note how the essence of his form comes from the application of the principles of efficient body mechanics. Watch the beginner or the awkward player and try to determine which principles he is not applying. Then take your own game and analyze it to see how it may be improved by the application of those same principles.

Day by day, consciously apply the principles of efficient body mechanics to everything you do. In a short time, efficient, effective movement will become a habit. Useless awkward motions will be eliminated, and all the body's energy will be directed toward accomplishing the greatest results with the least amount of effort. This is "good form"; this is graceful movement; this is efficiency.

PROJECTS FOR FURTHER STUDY

1. Go through the motions of performing each of the following tasks. First do the task awkwardly, as it might be done by an unskilled performer. Then do it as skillfully as you can, applying the principles of efficient body movement.
   Carrying a case of cokes
   Carrying a loaded tray in a cafeteria
   Standing on the streetcar, hanging onto a strap
   Dusting furniture
   Watering the lawn
   Scrubbing the ring off the bathtub
   Hoeing in the garden

Putting a log on the fire in the fireplace
Lifting a baby off the floor
Making a bed

2. For each task above, make a list of the principles of efficient movement which are applicable.

3. Watch a champion perform in some sport. List the principles of efficient movement which he applies.

4. Watch a highly skilled workman doing his work. List the ways in which he economizes his energy.

5. Watch someone working at a desk. First list the sources of fatigue, and then list at least three devices for relieving or delaying the onset of fatigue.

6. Do the same for a standing job.

10

The Balanced Posture: Sitting

THE NEW ENGLAND mother used to instruct her daughter: "A lady's back never touches the back of the chair." She was trying to train her daughter to sit *on* the chair, balancing the weight of her trunk over the seat of the chair. This defeated the entire purpose of sitting. Try sitting that way for a few minutes, then be glad that modern social custom now recognizes that chairs were made to be sat *in* not *on*.

Sitting may be either a resting posture or a working posture. As a resting posture it should be above all an energy saver, requiring minimum expenditure of energy because it utilizes to a maximum the support provided by the chair. As a working posture, it should combine minimum expenditure of energy with maximum freedom to move in accordance with the requirements of the task. The amount and kind of support varies with the kind of chair. The extent to which the available support is utilized varies with the reasons for assuming the sitting posture.

"Sit down and take a load off your feet." This common expression states only part of the reason for sitting. To be complete it should also read: "Sit down and take a load off your back." In standing, the problem of maintaining balance over a small base places a continual demand on the muscles of the body as the weight is continually shifted to keep the center of

178

gravity over the base of support. In sitting, this responsibility is largely taken over by the seat and back of the chair, which provide a larger supporting base close to the center of gravity of the body with additional props supplied by the chair back and arms.

Sitting for rest or relaxation is a compromise between standing up and the desire to lie down to escape the pull of gravity. The more nearly the entire body approaches the horizontal position, the greater is the degree of rest afforded to the tired muscles. Lounge chairs or "easy" chairs are designed to support the body in such a semireclining position. Padded to make them soft and inviting, they are slanted to allow the trunk to lean backward. The slanting chair back supports the weight of the body, so the muscles of the trunk can relax from their constant effort to hold the body erect. The chair seat is tilted slightly to raise the legs, thus forcing the weight of the body against the back of the chair, so the body is held snugly in the hollow of the chair. The chair back can do the work; the muscles no longer need to contract to resist the pull of gravity to keep the body from falling. If the legs are placed on a footstool which is the height of the chair seat, the muscles of the legs can also relax. With the entire body supported on a soft, comfortable surface, gravity works on the body only to hold it against the support of the chair. If the entire supporting surface of the chair is utilized, this is a position of rest (Figure 45).

If the entire surface of the chair is not utilized, the position becomes one of strain instead of rest. Some persons attempt to "sit long" and find themselves "sitting twice." They assume a position more nearly horizontal than the slant of the chair permits, with the result that the weight of the trunk is supported at only two points, the back of the sacrum and the middle of the upper back. The lower back is left unsupported and sagging in space. The shoulders and head are pushed forward, and the chin attempts to rest on the chest. The feet must be braced to keep the body from sliding out of the chair. This is

a deceptive position; it feels wonderfully comfortable and relaxed at first, but it soon becomes an awkward position of dis-

Fig. 45. When the entire supporting surface of the chair is utilized, sitting
is a position of rest. (*a*) With footstool; (*b*) feet on floor.

comfort and strain because the lower back has no support and
the abdominal muscles are stretched by the prodding of the
cramped abdominal viscera (Figure 46).

The general principle for the sitting posture of rest is, adapt the body to the contours of the chair to secure the maximum support from the chair. Lie down as far as the chair permits, but no farther. It is entirely within the bounds of good posture to lie fully extended on the davenport with pillows supporting the upper back and head; but to assume such a position without sup-

FIG. 46. "Sitting twice," which leaves the back unsupported, is a position of strain.

port under the shoulders throws additional work on the unsupported areas and brings fatigue instead of relaxation. If a chair is made for lounging, then lounge in it to the fullest extent possible. If a chair is made for semierect sitting, then the greatest comfort and rest will be achieved by sitting in a semierect position with the back resting along the back of the chair throughout its full length.

What about those favorite positions of sitting on one leg or throwing one leg over the arm of the chair? Neither is particularly graceful, but neither is particularly fatiguing if the basic principle of maximum support for the trunk is followed and the position is not held too long. The restless body seems to enjoy changes of position as an aid to circulation and the relief of tension. Any position held too long becomes fatiguing. The sitting-on-one-foot position quickly brings fatigue because the circulation of the leg is interfered with and the spine is twisted as it rises from the slanting pelvis. If this position becomes habitual, being assumed on every occasion for sitting, the muscles which hold the vertebrae in place tend also to adjust themselves to the twisted position, being stretched on one side and shortened on the other side. For long-continued sitting while reading or relaxing, it is far more restful to keep the legs in line with the body, preferably raising them from the floor and resting them on a footstool.

Sitting in a straight chair is less restful but provides greater freedom of movement. The weight of the trunk is borne by the buttocks and upper thighs, and the legs, relieved of the necessity for weight bearing, are used only for balance. In quiet sitting, when the hands are engaged in nothing more demanding than balancing a cup of tea, the back of the chair should be used for vertical support. Again the rule is, sit *in* the chair, not just *on* it. Sit back on the seat until the back of the buttocks touches the back of the chair; then the slightly slanting back of the chair provides support for the trunk and helps to keep it erect with a minimum amount of energy expenditure (Figures 47 and 48). Sliding forward on the seat in the C-curve position puts the base of support ahead of the center of gravity and leaves a length of the back hanging unsupported in space with the weight resting on the back of the sacrum and the shoulder blades (Figure 49). This position, sometimes described as "sitting on your liver," cramps and crowds the lungs and heart as well as the abdominal viscera and forces the wall of the abdomen forward into a most unattractive bulge. Sit this way for a few minutes and try to maintain a straight front line down the abdomen. Then slide back into the chair and notice how the bulge disappears without effort to control it. Less easy to observe, but equally apparent to others, is the spread at the level of the hips. It is difficult to keep the upper legs parallel while sitting in a C curve, and all semblance of gluteal control is lost in this awkward position. Sitting erect in the chair is not only more attractive, it is also less fatiguing, since the supporting surfaces of the chair are used to their fullest extent.

As for those troublesome legs, what should be done with

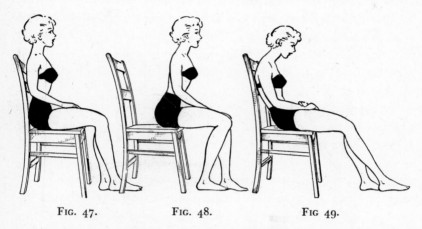

Fig. 47.   Fig. 48.   Fig 49.

Fig. 47. Sitting *in* a straight chair, using all the support it provides, is restful and graceful.

Fig. 48. Sitting *on* the edge of a straight chair is fatiguing.

Fig. 49. C-curve sitting leaves the back unsupported.

them? Must they be planted primly on the floor, at right angles to the body, feet parallel? This is a ladylike position but also a rather tiring one for many people because the thighs tend to rotate outward, throwing the knees away from each other, and constant effort must be exerted to keep the knees together. Modern custom very sensibly recognizes the propriety of sitting with the legs crossed, provided they are crossed gracefully. The principles of the balanced posture are not defied if the legs are crossed without tension and if an even distribution of weight over the base is maintained by bringing both legs closer to the mid-line.

While sitting erect in a straight chair, one leg may be crossed easily over the other above the knee, allowing the lower leg to hang without tension. Again, the position should not be held too long, because the pressure of the top leg interferes with the circulation to the lower leg. The position becomes bad both aesthetically and mechanically when the upper leg is twisted tightly around the lower leg with tension apparent in every line.

The legs also may be crossed at the ankles by allowing one

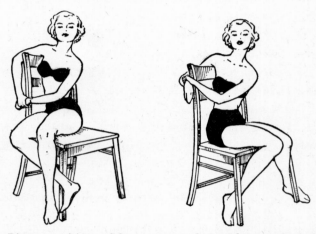

FIG. 50. Bizarre positions of legs, arms, and shoulders are both fatiguing and unattractive.

foot to rest lightly across the other one. But if this position is carried to the point of placing the outer borders of both feet on the floor, the rotation of the lower legs forces the knees apart, and again the muscles must maintain tension to hold the knees together.

Aesthetically, the poorest position of all is the one in which the calf of one leg is pressed tightly against the shin bone of the other. This not only spreads the calf and makes the leg look ungainly, but it can be held only with tension.

Bizarre positions of the feet and legs, twisting the legs around the legs of the chair, forcing the feet back over the rungs, and twisting the legs around each other like a pretzel are all positions of tension and strain (Figure 50). Relaxing the legs and placing them so that at least one foot is planted squarely on the floor to balance the body will do much to make sitting more restful—which is the real reason for sitting.

Much work is done in the sitting position, with the arms supported on a desk or table. In this position the trunk is slanted forward to bring the head and eyes over the task, and it is no longer possible to use the back of the chair for support, but the principles of the balanced posture still apply.

Try defying all the principles. Place the chair as far as possible from the desk. Perch on the edge of it with the body weight supported only by a narrow strip across the buttocks and the legs braced to keep the body from falling off the chair. Let the trunk collapse at the waistline, cramping the heart and lungs and forcing the back into a C curve with the head hanging perilously in space. Prop up the drooping shoulders and head by bracing the elbows on the table. Little wonder studying or writing is fatiguing in this position. The shoulders and neck begin to ache with strain; the buttocks become numb from pressure; and the cramped lungs and heart are hard pressed to maintain adequate circulation to the sleepy brain (Figure 51).

Then consider ways and means for securing maximum support while still retaining the greatest possible freedom of motion. Bring the chair well under the table, so close that the edge of the table almost touches the front of the body. Sit all the way back in the chair to distribute the weight of the trunk over the entire base of the buttocks, thus decreasing the pressure on any area. Let the trunk slant slightly forward from the hip joint to bring the eyes in line with the work being done, but keep the head-neck-trunk line as straight as possible for maximum support of the head. Rest the arms easily on the table, using them only for balance and not for strong support (Figure 52). At intervals, lean back against the chair back to relieve the strain of the held position. Watch that abdominal line; its outward bulge is the first sign that the back is beginning to sag

and the shoulders are beginning to droop. In this almost upright position the upper body is free to move, and the arms
may be moved easily to accomplish whatever task is at hand.

Quiet shifting of the body weight, movement of the legs, or
occasional forcible straightening of the shoulders will do much

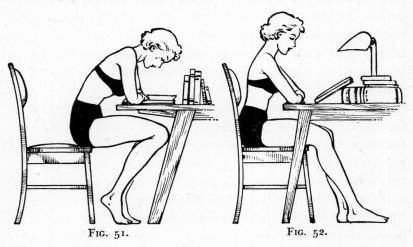

FIG. 51.   FIG. 52.

FIG. 51. Perching on the edge of the chair produces tension in feet, legs,
back, and shoulders.
FIG. 52. Sit all the way back in the chair, let the trunk slant slightly forward to bring the eyes over the work.

to increase comfort in sitting when the position must be held
for long periods of time. Any position, no matter how comfortable, if held too long induces a feeling of restraint, and even
slight movement provides a feeling of relief.

If your job requires that you remain seated for long periods,
try these specific motions for relief. Occasionally sit up as
straight as possible, contracting the abdominal muscles to force
the hollow of the back against the back of the chair. Force the
shoulders backward as far as they will go to stretch the muscles
of the chest wall and relieve the strain stretch on the muscles
which hold the scapulae in place. Let the head momentarily

lose its constant battle with gravity by dropping it forward as far as it will go toward the chest; then twist it to each side in turn to relieve the strain in the diagonal muscles of the back of the neck. Clasp both hands between the legs and pull downward to stretch the muscles of the back. Wiggle, shrug, and rotate the shoulders. Then, if possible, find some excuse for getting out of the chair for a few minutes to change the angle at the hip joint and let the shortened muscles resume their normal length. This is not time-wasting; a few minutes spent in making the body comfortable will pay big dividends in efficiency in working.

Much has been written about graceful attitudinizing in sitting down and rising from a chair. Most of it stems from an application of the basic principles of body dynamics discussed previously. Always prepare a new base before leaving the old; never throw weight against a joint; and use the strongest muscles available for any task. How do these apply in sitting down? First, get close enough to the chair so that the calf of one leg is touching it. Then place the toes of the other foot back under the edge of the chair for balance and support. In this position it is easy to lower the body to the chair, controlling the motion with the strong muscles of the leg. The body moves down in an almost erect position with the buttocks well over the chair seat but with no awkward bulges or protruberances.

Rising is simply a reversal of the process. Place one foot forward and the other slightly back with the toes on the ground and the heel raised. Pushing with the back leg, the body rises easily and the weight is transferred to the front foot, ready for the first step of walking away.

Standing too far away from the chair before sitting produces a number of hazards. One poor technique involves bending the trunk forward to maintain balance while the buttocks are pushed backward to find the supporting surface. This is awkward and involves a number of extra wiggles and hunches to finally get the back of the body to the back of the chair. The opposite, and perhaps more dangerous, method is to put full faith in the presence and immovability of the chair and throw the body weight backward, allowing it to light on the chair with a bounce. Unless this is unusually well timed, the result is a wide space between the back of the body and the back of the chair, again necessitating extra wiggles and hitches to bring the body into alignment.

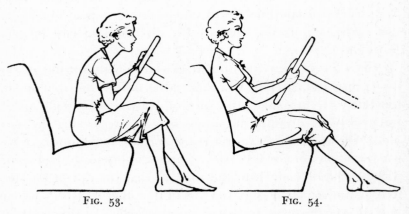

FIG. 53.   FIG. 54.

FIG. 53. Sitting on the edge of the seat with the body cramped over the wheel and the head forward to peer through the windshield is fatiguing. FIG. 54. Utilize the entire supporting surface of the seat, relax, and let the road come to you.

Lounge chairs do pose a special problem for downsitting and uprising. They are too low, too deep, and too soft to make graceful sitting and rising easy. Avoid trying to rise directly from the depths of the chair, for this necessitates pulling and tugging with the arms to get the center of gravity far enough forward so that the pushing force of the legs can act through it. The best solution is to follow the principles outlined above and then add an extra slide backward into the seat after sitting or an extra push forward to the edge of the chair before rising.

Some comments should be made about sitting posture while

driving a car, particularly when the position must be held for a long period of time. Nothing could be more futile or fatiguing than perching nervously on the edge of the driver's seat, gripping the wheel with tense fingers, and peering forward with the nose almost touching the windshield (Figure 53). Here, too, greater comfort and less strain will result from application of the principle of deriving maximum support from all available surfaces. Sit well back in the seat. If the legs are too short to reach the pedals, then either move the seat forward or place a cushion behind the back to bring the body forward on the seat. The important thing is to make sure that the back is in contact with the car cushions throughout its entire length. The free arms, moving easily from the shoulder, are strong enough to control the modern car in all normal situations. Then resist the urge to peer ahead, trying to see "just a little bit farther." The three inches increase in range of vision is a high price to pay for stiff and stretched neck and shoulder muscles. Sit back with the head easily balanced over the shoulders and let the road come to you (Figure 54).

If driving must be continued for long periods of time without rest, use the tricks described above to relieve the strain and tension. Forcibly contract the abdominal muscles, shrug the shoulders, and shift the weight from side to side to change the position of the hip joint. And remember to let the car do the work. Just relax and guide it—don't mentally push it every mile of the way.

Whatever may be the reason for sitting—working, reading, listening, resting, or lounging—the advice offered by a fine old man who was still working constructively at eighty is applicable:

> When you work, work easy;
> When you sit, sit loose;
> When you start worrying, go to sleep.

PROJECTS FOR FURTHER STUDY

1. *a.* Sit on a chair in a posture appropriate for a formal tea.
   b. Sit on the floor in a posture appropriate for an evening around
      the camp fire.
   Compare the two postures? Is either more "correct" than the
   other? Are both postures balanced? Do both postures serve the
   purpose of the occasion?

2. Sitting on a straight chair, slide down until the end of your spine
   is at the front edge of the chair. Hold the position for ten minutes. Is it comfortable? Where do you feel fatigue? What is supporting your back?

3. Sit in an overstuffed "easy chair" with your back straight and
   your feet parallel on the floor. Hold this position for ten minutes. Is it comfortable? Where do you feel fatigue? Why?

4. For one day, critically observe the sitting postures of the people
   around you. How many of them are getting maximum support
   from the chairs they are sitting in? How many of them are in a
   position of strain and fatigue? How many of them are sitting in
   postures appropriate for the situation? Write a paper describing
   "Sitting Postures I have Seen."

CHAPTER

11

The Balanced Posture: Evaluation

No two human beings are built exactly alike. This must be remembered when an attempt is made to evaluate the posture of any individual. The posture which is normal and "right" for A may be a position of strain for B. True, everyone has arms, legs, head, neck, and trunk arranged in the same general pattern. All have approximately the same number of bones, muscles, and nerves. But within this general framework there are many differences of proportion, structure, and relationships.

One of the more immediately obvious differences is the length of the leg in relation to the length of the trunk. The dressmaker's model on whom any dress achieves added style is usually long-legged, with a short trunk and narrow pelvic girdle. Her sartorially less fortunate sister may be of the same height but have a trunk three inches longer and legs three inches shorter. She may have narrow hips or broad, but she will always be described as "dumpy." Masculine counterparts may be seen in the long-legged basketball player or high jumper as contrasted with the more stockily built typical football hero.

The very shape of the vertebrae which make up the back, be it long or short, also differs in different individuals. The typical vertebra of the upper back is slightly thicker in back than it is in front. When these slightly wedge-shaped vertebrae are stacked on each other, a slight backward curve is formed, giving the normally rounded upper back. If the slope of the vertebra is exaggerated even slightly, the outward curve of the upper back is increased. If the top and bottom of the vertebrae are more nearly parallel, the upper back is straight and flat.

The proportionate lengths of the clavicle and scapula also differ. A relatively short clavicle matched with a relatively long scapula makes it almost impossible for the person to throw back his shoulders and "straighten up." If the clavicle is relatively longer than the scapula, the shoulders are held back easily; in fact, it is difficult to let them droop forward.

In the lower back, the vertebrae are typically thicker in front and thinner in back, producing the forward curve of the "normal" lower back. Again, the slope of these wedges varies in different individuals. If the slope is increased, the forward curve of the lower back is exaggerated, giving the typical hollow back. If the slope is decreased, as it often is, the lower back is almost straight and the individual is said to be straight-backed.

One of the most noticeable variations occurs in the slope of the sacrum and the angle at which it is attached to the last lumbar vertebra. The angle may be acute, causing the sacrum to slope sharply rearward, and the person finds it difficult to rotate the pelvic girdle far enough to "tuck his tail under." If this is coupled with the acutely curved lower back, the individual will find it impossible to flatten his back to the floor. No matter how strongly he contracts his gluteal and abdominal muscles to bring the lower back to the floor, a space will always remain between the back and the floor. In another individual, the situation may be reversed. The sacrum appears to slope forward, giving a flat continuous line from the lower back down past the buttocks.

The angle the long thigh bone makes with its head and the angle at which the head is inserted in the socket in the pelvic girdle is another point of variation. Some legs naturally slope inward at a sharp angle, while others are more nearly parallel.

Some thigh bones are slightly twisted, rotating the leg to such a degree that it is normal for the person to "toe out" slightly in the standing position. Less common is the reverse rotation, which produces a normal pigeon-toed position.

Variations in general body build are so numerous that it is impossible to describe them. Wide shoulders, narrow hips; narrow shoulders, wide hips; evenly matched shoulders and hips; long necks, short necks; slim waists, thick waists; long heavy arms, short slim arms; heavy bulging muscles, long slim muscles—the possible variations and combinations are almost infinite in number. Every human being differs slightly from every other human being. Each has his own peculiar posture problems.

What, then, is the "best" posture? There is no single best posture for all individuals. Each person must take the body he has and make the best of it. For each person the best posture is that in which the body segments are balanced in the position of least strain and maximum support. This is an individual matter.

The check list shown in Figure 55 has been prepared to aid in checking the balance of individual postures in standing, walking, and working. Carefully used, it will indicate the major zigs and zags in the body, and rightly interpreted it can indicate which zigs and zags are normal for the individual and which are simply the result of poor postural habits.

Three people should work together to check one another's posture, each two in turn checking and discussing the posture of the third.

Begin with the standing position. Have the person whose posture is being checked assume either his "best" or his "habitual" posture. (It is better to work with the habitual posture, but awareness of being under observation makes the subject self-conscious, and invariably he will try to correct any defects of which he is aware. Actually, habitual posture can be observed only when the person is not aware that he is being checked.)

First observe the feet from the front. If the feet are parallel, check in the column marked *Straight*. If they are slightly toed-out, check in the first column under *Out*. If the toeing-out is

CHECK LIST FOR BALANCED POSTURE

Name_____ Date_____

	In	Straight	Out
Feet			
Ankles			

	Backward	Balanced	Forward
Knees			
Pelvis			
Abdomen			
Chest			
Shoulders			
Head			
Body line			

FIG. 55. The zigzag check list for balanced posture.

marked, check in the last column to the right. Similarly, if the toes point inward slightly, check in the first column under *In;* if the toeing-in is pronounced, check in the last column to the left.

To observe the ankles, view the feet from the rear and note

the position of the ankle bone (malleolus) and the heel cord. If the feet appear to be rolled inward so that the ankle bones point downward, check in the appropriate column under *In*. Occasionally feet will be found in which the foot appears to be rolled outward and the ankle bones point slightly upward, but the inward position is much more common. If the foot rolls neither inward nor outward, check in the column headed *Straight*.

To determine the extent to which it is anatomically possible for the individual to correct any deviations which may be noted, have him place his foot in the *Straight*, or balanced, position. If pointing the toes straight forward produces a feeling of strain or pain, then correction should not be attempted without orthopedic diagnosis. If the balanced position merely feels uncomfortable because it seems strange, then it is likely that the unbalanced position is only habitual and can be altered to bring the foot into better alignment.

In attempting to correct an inward rotation of the ankle, most persons will throw the weight to the outside of the foot by gripping with the toes. This is not a true correction for the lowered arch, and it is almost impossible to hold the arch and ankle up in this manner. The rotation actually starts as far up as the hip joint, and to be effective the correction must be made with the whole leg. The thigh bone must be rotated outward, throwing the knees to a more nearly outward position, thus raising the arch of the foot. If this position can be held without strain, the lowered arch is the result of poor body mechanics. If pain and strain occur, then the lowered arch and inwardly rotated ankles are probably structural rather than habitual, and the orthopedist should be consulted as to the best means for dealing with this structural problem. A slight lift under the heel, a small wedge inserted inside the sole of the shoe, or a supporting arch built into the shoe will do much to relieve the strain which this apparently slight deviation creates, a strain which affects the comfort of the entire body.

In this evaluation, the height of the arch is not important. Feet may be perfectly balanced mechanically with very high arches; they may also be comfortable and functionally effective with arches so low that the whole foot appears to be flat. The important consideration is the degree to which the foot has rolled inward or outward.

The knees should be viewed from the side to determine whether they are "locked" backward, relaxed and balanced, or flexed. Flexed knees will be found seldom unless the individual is trying to correct a habitual locking of the knees in the hyper-extended position. The knees are *Backward* if the whole leg appears to make a continuous curve from the ankle to above the knee. If the knee is easy and relaxed in the balanced position, the curve will be broken at the knee joint. To test the degree of hyperextension, hold the hand about one-half inch behind the knee joints and ask the subject to throw the knees backward. If the knee is relaxed, this much backward motion is easily possible; if the knee is locked, no further motion backward can be made. If the knees are balanced and relaxed, check in the middle column. If the possible backward motion is slight, check in the first column under *Backward;* if no motion is possible, check in the extreme left column. If the knees appear to be actually bent, check in the appropriate column under *Forward*. Knee position is usually both habitual and related to some other unbalanced segment of the body. Reserve judgment until the rest of the check is completed.

The *Balanced* pelvis rests directly under the trunk in a position to give maximum support to the contents of the abdominal cavity. If the buttocks jut markedly backward, check the pelvis as being in the *Backward* position. To determine to what extent this deviation is structural, ask the person being checked to attempt to rotate the pelvic girdle to bring the coccyx downward and forward by using the abdominal muscles. If the pelvis moves easily into the balanced position and the "shelf" disappears, leaving only a mild outcurve, then it is probable that the position of the pelvis is habitual rather than structural. If the "shelf" can be made to disappear only by "tucking" until the knees flex and the person appears to be sitting down while standing up, then it is reasonable to assume that the backward position is normal for the individual and cannot be completely corrected.

The *Forward* position of the pelvis is sometimes found in persons who have practiced "tucking" overconscientiously in an attempt to conceal the muscular bulge of the buttocks. It is usually accompanied by slightly flexed knees. Occasionally it occurs as a structural deviation accompanying an unusually flat or forward-sloping sacrum. Again, determine the amount of effort required to bring the pelvis into the balanced position under the trunk. If the correction can be made easily, it should be practiced until it becomes habitual.

The designations of *Forward* and *Backward* for abdomen are descriptive rather than anatomical. *Forward* means protruding in a curve beyond the flat line of the body. *Backward* means that the abdomen has been "sucked in" in a mistaken attempt to improve the appearance. The *Balanced* abdomen is neither concave nor convex, and any concavity or convexity is very rarely structural. The position of the abdomen is closely related to the position of the pelvic girdle, and both corrections must be made simultaneously.

The *Backward* chest is flat and sunken; the *Forward* chest is held out in a rigid and exaggerated position. The *Balanced* chest is in the intermediate position, up, not out, and held easily in a relaxed manner. Many structural variations in chest walls will be noted. Some ribs are attached to the sternum so that they form a flat, continuous line; others will bulge and bow outwards; still others slope back sharply from the sternum. These structural variations are of no particular concern, but they should be considered in checking the chest position.

The shoulders are *Forward* if they droop forward past the line of the clavicle; *Backward* if they are held rigidly in the exaggerated military posture. They are *Balanced* if they hang easily in line with the ears, so that the arms hang close to the sides of the body. Again the test for correctibility is the ease with which the shoulders may be moved into the balanced position. The individual with short clavicles will find this difficult; so will the individual with heavily developed muscles running from the shoulders to the chest. The muscles can be stretched by appropriate exercise, but if the clavicles are short, the *Forward* position of the shoulders is normal for the individual. Shoulders carried *Backward* to such an extent that they seem almost to overhang in back are usually the result of structure rather than habit. Extreme military training at an early age may produce this posture, but it is usually lost when the training is discontinued.

A *Forward* head is easily discernible by the slope of the neck and often by the double chin which is caused by the sagging folds of flesh in front. Be careful in correcting it that the *Backward* head does not result. A *Backward* head is one in which the chin is raised and pointed outward until the throat line becomes taut. In the *Balanced* head the neck rises vertically from the back of the shoulders, and the chin is tucked in so that it makes a right angle with the front of the neck. Some normally *Forward* heads will be found in conjunction with a rounded upper back, but the majority of them are the result of habit and can be corrected.

When all the segments have been checked, then observe the slope of the long line of the body. Does it appear to slope slightly *Forward* from heels to head? Does the weight appear to be resting on the heels in the *Backward* position? Or does the body rise vertically from the floor in an upright straight line? The *Forward* or *Backward* position is usually a final compensation for some other imbalance, and it is usually a matter of habit which can be corrected.

If the check has been made with reasonable accuracy, it will show the zigzag nature of unbalanced posture. In general, if certain segments have been checked as *Forward,* then others will be found to be *Backward* as the body compensates in order to maintain its total balance. This emphasizes the need for aligning the total body in achieving the balanced posture and indicates the futility of trying to correct the deviation of an isolated segment without considering its relation to the rest of the body.

When all three persons have been checked, repeat the process with the subjects in motion. Have the person being observed walk easily back and forth a few times to relieve his feeling of stiffness in being observed, then, as he walks, again check feet, ankles, knees, pelvis, abdomen, chest, shoulders, head, and total body line. Some bad habits which may have been corrected in the static observation tend to crop out again when the body is in motion. Again suggest techniques for correction based on the balanced posture in walking (Chapter 8) and determine the ease or difficulty of applying them.

The third and final check should be made with the person performing some simple task which involves lifting, reaching, or carrying. Again observe the relationship of the body segments. Is the pelvis kept in its proper position under the trunk (FPT)? Does the head maintain its balanced position on the shoulders? Does the abdomen suddenly bulge forward with the act of lifting or carrying a weight? Do the shoulders droop forward as the hands and arms are engaged in a task? The exact positions of the body segments will be determined by the nature of the task, of course, but it is easy to observe the degree to which balance is maintained throughout the entire task, as well as the degree to which the body appears strained and awkward.

It is not important that the checking be scientifically accurate to the *n*th degree. The value of the check lies in focusing the attention of the individual on the observable deviations of his body from the easy posture of balance.

In the checking process the observers may note such deviations as a lateral curvature of the spine, a twisting of the spine, a high shoulder, or a high hip. These may be called to the attention of the individual, but they are not noted on the check slip, since their correction lies beyond the scope of the untrained individual. It may, however, be helpful to the individual to have these deviations noted, since they may be causing pain or strain and should be referred to the orthopedic physician for diagnosis and remedy if possible.

In any event, the checking process will make the individual much more aware of himself as an individual, with his own good and bad points. This self-knowledge is the beginning of improvement.

PROJECTS FOR FURTHER STUDY

1. Ask two persons of about the same height to stand side by side. Compare them as to leg length, shoulder width, spinal curves, neck length, and weight. Are there differences which might be related to the "normal" posture of each?
2. Observe the people around you, trying to find one who appears to have a normally round back; a normally flat back; a structural sway-back; unusually long clavicles; unusualy short clavicles; a structural forward head. In each instance note how this structure affects the posture of the individual.
3. Ask several right-handed people to stand against a wall so that you can observe how many of them have one shoulder lower than the other? Which shoulder is it?
4. Using the same people, observe how many of them have one hip which appears to be more prominent or higher than the other. Ask them to turn around so that you can try to trace the line of the spinal column as it joins the sacrum. Is it perfectly straight, or does it appear to slant? Ask how many of them have ever had their legs measured to determine whether they are both the same length? Ask how many of them have ever experienced lower-back pain. Comment on your findings.

5. Working with two other persons, use the evaluation chart to check one another's postures standing, walking, lifting an object, and reaching above the head. Discuss the findings with one another and make suggestions for improvement, where needed.

6. While sitting listening to a lecturer, a preacher, a teacher, or a performer, mentally check their posture on the evaluation chart. Briefly describe your observations.

Part IV

APPENDIX

Suggested Exercises

THE FOLLOWING list of exercises is representative rather than all-inclusive. There are thousands of other exercises which might be performed with equal effectiveness. This list includes appropriate samples of the various kinds of exercise referred to in the text. It is not expected that any one person will do all of them at any one time; they are presented for use as needed.

In some instances the successive movements of the exercise have been lettered for greater clarity of presentation. In no instance does this imply that they are to be performed "to the count." They should be done at the speed and rhythm best suited to each individual, the rhythm being maintained by the use of descriptive phrases, such as "Push, and push, and bounce, and push" or "Swing, swing, swing over, and hold."

Many of these exercises are done either lying or sitting on the floor. It is desirable to use some sort of a mat, but where none is available, a bath towel spread on the floor makes a very acceptable substitute.

1. CAT STRETCHING
    Lying or standing.
    Stretch and twist and squirm and yawn. Mimic a cat waking up
        from a nap.

    To release tension of held position. To facilitate capillary circulation.
2. DIAGONAL STRETCHING
    Lying on back, arms overhead, legs extended and parallel.
    a. Reach up with right arm while pushing down with left heel,
        making body long on one diagonal and short on the other.

b. Reverse position, reaching with left arm and pushing down with right heel.

To relieve tension of held position. To activate diagonal abdominal muscles.

3. STANDING BOUNCE STRETCH
   Standing, arms at sides, feet slightly apart.
   Curl head and shoulders forward, allowing arms to dangle. Let weight of arms pull trunk forward with a slight "bounce" as trunk moves down, up slightly, down a little farther, up, down, continuing until backs of hands are slapping on floor. Keep abdominal muscles firm. Keep knees relaxed. (If the knees are kept straight or locked, this changes the entire effect of the exercises. The old familiar exercise of "touch the floor without bending the knees" is primarily a stretcher for the muscles of the back of the upper and lower legs.)

   To loosen and limber trunk muscles preparatory to more strenuous exercise. To relieve tension. To improve tone of abdominal muscles.

4. STANDING STRETCH AND FALL
   Standing, arms overhead, feet slightly apart.
   a. Reach up with hands stretching as tall and thin as possible.
   b. Continue upward stretch until heels rise from the ground.
   c. Release stretch and let trunk and arms fall forward until backs of hands are lying limply on the floor.

   To relieve tension. To give gentle progressive contraction and release to extensor muscles of back.

5. PROGRESSIVE ABDOMINAL SERIES (1)
   Lying on back, knees bent and together, feet on floor close to buttocks.
   a. Flatten lower back to floor by contracting abdominal and gluteal muscles to rotate pelvis so that the tip of the coccyx rotates forward, upward.
   b. Relax.
   c. Repeat, concentrating on the feeling of rotating the pelvis.

   To improve tonus and control of abdominal muscles. To develop kinesthetic perception of rotating pelvis.

6. PROGRESSIVE ABDOMINAL SERIES (2)

   Lying on back, legs parallel and extended.

   a. Flatten lower back to floor by contracting gluteal and abdominal muscles to rotate pelvis so that tip of coccyx rotates forward, upward.

   b. Relax.

   c. Repeat, concentrating on the feeling of rotating the pelvis.

   To improve tonus and control of abdominal muscles. To develop kinesthetic perception of rotating pelvis.

7. PROGRESSIVE ABDOMINAL SERIES (3)

   Lying face down, legs parallel and extended.

   a. Flatten lower back by contracting abdominal and gluteal muscles to raise abdominal wall from floor.

   b. Relax.

   c. Repeat.

   To strengthen abdominal muscles by forcing them to work against the pull of gravity. To improve ability to control action of abdominal muscles.

8. PROGRESSIVE ABDOMINAL SERIES (4)

   On hands and knees, head hanging down.

   a. Hump lower back by contracting abdominal and gluteal muscles to flatten abdominal wall.

   b. Relax.

   c. Repeat.

   To strengthen abdominal muscles by forcing them to work against gravity while in a disadvantageous position. To improve ability to control action of abdominal muscles.

9. PROGRESSIVE ABDOMINAL SERIES (5) (Cat Breathing)

   On hands and knees, head hanging down.

   a. Hump lower back by contracting abdominal and gluteal muscles to flatten abdominal wall.

   b. Hold contraction and inhale deeply with mouth open.

   c. Still holding contraction, exhale slowly and as completely as possible.

   d. Relax.

e. Repeat, hump, and breathe, and blow, and relax.

To strengthen abdominal muscles by forcing them to work against gravity while in a disadvantageous position and in resistance to excursion of diaphram. To improve ability to control action of abdominal muscles.

10. PELVIC ROCK

Standing, arms at side, knees relaxed.

Place hands on hips so that index fingers rest on the small protuberances on front rim of the pelvic girdle, thumbs pointing down and backward.

a. Push downward and backward with index fingers while pulling forward and upward with thumbs to rotate pelvic girdle so that coccyx moves backward and upward.

b. Reverse the push and pull to rotate pelvic girdle so that coccyx moves downward and forward.

c. Move pelvis forward and backward through its full range of motion.

d. Remove hands from hips and again rotate pelvis forward and backward.

e. Bring pelvis to rest in balanced position, neither forward nor backward.

To develop kinesthetic perception. To improve ability to keep pelvis in balanced position.

11. CURL SIT-UP—LONG LYING

Lying on back, arms at side, legs extended and parallel.

a. Bring head and shoulders forward, curling up into sitting position without use of hands.

b. Return to lying position by gradually uncurling body, beginning at lower back.

c. Repeat as slowly as possible, taking ten or more counts to come up and same count to return.

To strengthen abdominal muscles.

12. CURL SIT-UP—HOOK LYING

Lying on back, arms at side, knees bent, and feet as close to buttocks as possible.

a. Bring head and shoulders forward, attempting to curl up into sitting position without use of hands and without moving feet.

b. Return to lying position.

c. Repeat as slowly as possible.

To strengthen abdominal muscles.

13. TIRED BUSINESS MAN'S SERIES

(These exercises were first described by Dr. Arthur H. Steinhaus, with the explanation that the modern businessman—or woman—tends to fall apart at three points: his back, his belly, and his bunions. This series of towel exercises was devised to strengthen these three weakest points. It was designed to be done daily, before or after the morning shower, utilizing the readily available bath towel as an aid.)

a. For the Back

Fold a bath towel lengthwise into fourths. In good standing position, place towel across back of neck, grasping one end in each hand shoulder-high, keeping elbows down.

(1) Pull forward strongly with both hands, resisting the pull by pushing head back, chin down and in. If pull and resistance are equal, no motion will occur.

(2) Release pull and relax neck and shoulder muscles.

(3) Repeat.

To strengthen extensor muscles of neck and upper back.

b. For the Belly

Fold a bath towel lengthwise into thirds. In good standing position, place towel across lower back, grasping one end with each hand in front of body.

(1) Pull forward strongly with both hands, resisting the pull by contracting abdominal muscles. If pull and resistance are equal, no motion will occur.

(2) Release pull and relax abdominal muscles.

(3) Repeat.

To strengthen abdominal muscles.

c. For the Bunions

Fold a bath towel in half lengthwise. Place towel under one foot with about two inches extending beyond toes. Grasp

an end of towel in each hand, hands in line with so-called
"metatarsal arch."

(1) Pull upward strongly with hands, resisting the pull by
curling toes down. If pull and resistance are equal, no
motion will occur.

(2) Release pull and relax foot and toe muscles. Shake foot
to relieve possible cramps.

(3) Repeat.

To strengthen small muscles of foot.

14. RESISTANCE PULL-DOWN

Standing. Raise both arms above head, pulling shoulder blades
together to keep shoulders back. Clench fists.

a. Slowly pull fists down to shoulder level, making hard work
of it by resisting the pull as much as possible.

b. Still keeping fists clenched, push arms up above head, using
maximum resistance.

c. Relax arms and let them drop limply to sides.

To strengthen arm and shoulder muscles.

15. RESISTANCE PUSH AND PULL

Standing. Bring clenched fists to shoulder level.

a. Slowly push fists forward, resisting push as strongly as possible.

b. Still keeping fists clenched, pull them back to shoulders,
using maximum resistance.

c. Relax arms and let them drop limply to sides.

To strengthen pushing and pulling muscles.

16. HAND FIGHT

Standing. Clasp hands, chest height, elbows at shoulder level.

a. Pull strongly, letting each hand resist the other.

b. Relax.

c. Pull again.

To strengthen muscles which hold shoulders back.

17. UNFOLD AND HOLD

Sitting, knees bent, feet as close to buttocks as possible.

Wrap arms around bent legs and curl head and trunk forward
until head is resting on knees. Gradually uncurl spine, be-

ginning with head and upper back. As back straightens, stretch as tall as possible, pushing up through top of head and resisting the extension with the pulling arms. As top of stretch is reached, with abdominal muscles in maximum contraction, release arms and slowly raise them sideward, while attempting to maintain maximum trunk-stretch position with abdominal contraction.

To improve ability to control action of abdominal muscles. To increase tone of abdominal muscles and extensor muscles of upper back.

18. SITTING STRETCH WITH ARM RAISING

Sitting cross-legged, back straight.

Stretch trunk as tall as possible, pushing up through top of head and keeping chin in. At maximum stretch, attempt to hold position while slowly raising arms sideward, upward, then lowering them back to sides.

To improve ability to control action of abdominal muscles. To increase tone of abdominal muscles.

9. KNEE SIDE FALL

Lying on back, arms extended at sides. Bend legs to bring knees close to chest.

a. Keeping shoulders flat on floor and legs bent and together, let legs fall to left until left knee touches floor.

b. Bring bent legs back to chest.

c. Let bent legs fall to right until right knee touches floor.

d. Bring legs back to chest.

To activate diagonal abdominal muscles. To apply twist and squeeze pressure to abdominal viscera.

20. KNEE-HOLD ROCKER

Lying on back, bring knees to chest and clasp arms around legs to hold them in close contact with body.

Rock forward and backward, trying to sit up while holding legs close to body.

To strengthen abdominal muscles. To apply pressure to abdominal viscera.

21. SITTING KNEE FALL

    Sitting, leaning back with weight on hands, knees bent and
      together, feet close to buttocks.
    a. Let both legs fall to right until right knee touches floor,
      while twisting trunk to left.
    b. Return to starting position.
    c. Repeat to left.
    d. Continue, gradually increasing speed.

    To strengthen abdominal muscles. To apply pressure to ab-
      dominal viscera.

22. HIP WALKING

    Sitting, back straight, arms crossed on chest, legs extended and
      parallel.
    a. Contract gluteal muscles strongly and rock to left.
    b. With right leg lifted enough to permit heel to clear floor
      and knee straight, reach forward with heel and place it on
      floor in advance of left foot.
    c. Rock to right and advance left foot in same manner.
    d. Repeat, "walking" body forward.
    e. Reverse action and "walk" backward.

    To increase tonus and control of gluteal and abdominal muscles.
      Some twisting squeeze of abdominal viscera.

23. ROCK AND FALL

    Sitting, back straight, legs extended and parallel. Raise arms to
      bring elbows to shoulder height, finger tips touching, palms
      out, at chest height.
    a. Contract gluteal muscles to rock body to right.
    b. Rock to left.
    c. Continue, rocking farther each time.
    d. As you rock to left, twist trunk and let body fall until back
      is parallel with floor, catching weight on palms of hands.
    e. Maintaining hand and shoulder position, push off strongly
      to start the rock and fall to right.
    f. Continue, push, and rock, and fall, gradually increasing
      speed.

    To exercise diagonal abdominal muscles and apply twist and
      squeeze to abdominal viscera.

24. SIDE WINDER

Standing, arms raised sideward, feet slightly apart.

a. Begin twisting trunk slightly to right, keeping arm-shoulder line straight and without moving hips or legs.

b. Return to starting position.

c. Twist a little farther.

d. Return.

e. Continue, twisting a little more each time until you can see wall in back of you.

f. Hold position of greatest twist.

g. Release and return to starting position.

h. Repeat to left.

To activate diagonal muscles of trunk. To apply twisting pressure to abdominal viscera.

25. AIRPLANE

Lying on back, arms extended shoulder height, legs spread apart.

a. Raise right leg to a vertical position.

b. Drop right leg across body attempting to touch toes to extended left hand.

c. Bring leg back to vertical position.

d. Lower leg to floor.

e. Repeat with left leg and right arm. Keep shoulders and arms on floor throughout the exercise, twisting trunk to bring leg across body.

To activate diagonal muscles of abdominal wall. To increase flexibility.

26. GIANT ROCKER

Sitting, arms at sides, legs extended and parallel.

a. Rock onto back, allowing legs to rise slightly from floor.

b. Bring legs down to start rock forward.

c. Continue rocking, increasing leg lift each time until legs are over head and toes rest on floor behind head.

To invert body. To stimulate circulation. To stretch and tone muscles of back. To increase flexibility.

27. SPLIT STRETCH

Sitting, legs apart.

a. Bend forward from hip joints, placing both hands lightly on left leg. Slide hands down leg as far as they will go easily. "Bounce" back slightly, then slide hands a little farther. Continue bounce, slide, bounce, slide, gradually pulling head and shoulders forward until head touches knee.

b. Repeat to right.

To increase flexibility and range of motion in back and hip joints.

28. LEG SWING AND KICK

Partners standing side by side. Inside hands on each other's shoulders.

a. Begin swinging inside legs easily back and forth. Gradually extend the amplitude of the swing, bringing legs higher and higher. As toes begin to reach shoulder height, extend outside arms forward at shoulder level and attempt to kick fingers with toes. Continue to rhythm of "swing, swing, and kick."

b. Change sides and repeat.

To increase flexibility of hip joint.

29. SHOULDER CIRCLING

Sitting, cross-legged, back erect, hands lying loosely in lap.

a. Circle right shoulder, forward, upward, backward, downward, allowing relaxed arm to follow movement of shoulder.

b. Reverse direction of circle, backward, upward, forward, downward.

c. Repeat with left shoulder.

d. Repeat with both shoulders simultaneously.

e. Repeat with shoulders moving in opposite directions.

To increase flexibility of shoulder joint. To relieve tension. To develop kinesthetic perception.

30. SWAN

Face lying, legs extended, arms at sides.

a. Clasp hands behind back. Pull down strongly with hands and arms until head and shoulders are off mat.

b. Release slightly, then pull again, a little harder.

c. Relax, and repeat.

To strengthen muscles that pull shoulders back.

31. LIE—SIT—STAND

Lying on back, arms crossed on chest, legs fully extended.

a. Curl forward to sitting position, crossing legs as you come up.

b. Rock body forward over crossed legs and come to standing position without using hands.

c. Sit down, still without using hands.

d. Lie back, extending legs.

e. Repeat as rapidly as possible.

To improve coordination, flexibility, and ability to control body movement. To stimulate circulation.

32. SWING OVER AND HOLD

Standing, feet slightly apart, arms at sides.

Let arms swing slowly back and forth in front of body, each swing covering a slightly longer arc as momentum increases. As arms reach highest possible swing, let them make complete circle passing in front of face. Continue swinging right, left, circle, and hesitate, to rhythm of "Swing, swing, swing over, and hold." Gradually increase amplitude of swing, letting trunk bend forward on downswing and stretching up on upswing until hands are touching floor on down swing. Then decrease amplitude of swing gradually until arms are again barely moving across erect body.

To increase flexibility. To stimulate circulation.

33. JUMPING JACK

Standing, feet together, arms at sides.

a. Jump feet apart while clapping hands together overhead.

b. Jump feet together while clapping hands together behind back. Continue rhythmically, gradually increasing tempo.

To stimulate circulation.

34. COACHMAN'S SWING

Sitting, cross-legged, back erect, strong abdominal contraction. Extend arms to sides, then vigorously wrap them around body as far as they will go. Extend, wrap, pushing shoulders farther back on each extension.

To stimulate circulation. To increase flexibility of shoulder joint. To activate extensor muscles of upper back.

35. Hip Lift

Lying on back, arms at sides, knees bent and together, feet as close to buttocks as possible.

a. Strongly contract abdominal muscles to rotate coccyx forward and upward. Continue movement by gradually raising back from floor, vertebra by vertebra, until body weight is resting on shoulders and feet and body is in straight line from knees to shoulders.

b. Let body sag slightly and hang between knees and shoulders like a hammock.

c. Straighten body by "picking up the tuck" and gradually return to lying position, coming down vertebra by vertebra.

d. As hips touch floor, let legs slide down to the extended position.

Begin this exercise by taking twenty slow counts to rise and twenty counts to return. As control is improved, take sixty counts up and sixty counts down.

To induce relaxation. To improve ability to control action of abdominal muscles. To give muscles and ligaments of back a gentle stretch.

36. Head Turning

Sitting cross-legged, back straight.

To count of thirty, turn head slowly to right as far as it will go. To second count of thirty, turn it back to forward position. Repeat to left. Keep movement continuous and controlled. Keep chin in. Keep eyes closed.

To induce relaxation and develop kinesthetic perception.

37. Arm Turning

Lying on back, legs extended and together, arms at side, palms up.

To count of thirty, slowly turn arms from palms-up position to palms-down position. To second count of thirty, return arms to palms-up position. Movement should be rotation about long axis of arm, extending to shoulder joint. Keep movement continuous and controlled.

To induce relaxation. To develop kinesthetic perception.

38. LEG TURNING

Lying on back, legs extended and together, ankles touching.

To count of thirty, slowly turn legs from position in which ankles and big toes are touching to position in which outer borders of feet and little toes are touching floor. To second count of thirty, slowly return legs to original position. Movement should be rotation about long axis of legs, extending to hip joint. Keep movement continuous and controlled.

To induce relaxation. To develop kinesthetic perception.

39. RELAXED ROLL

Lying on back, arms extended overhead on floor, legs extended and parallel.

a. Keeping arms and shoulders on floor, begin rolling right hip and leg across body to left. Continue roll until right shoulder and arm are pulled off floor.

b. Just as body is about to topple over, relax and let body flop limply back to original position.

c. Repeat with left hip leading.

To give diagonal stretch. To induce relaxation.

40. SLEEP MAKER

Lying on back, arms at sides, knees bent and together, feet close to buttocks.

a. Flatten lower back by contracting abdominal and gluteal muscles.

b. Hold contraction as long as possible while consciously inhaling and exhaling at normal rhythm.

c. Relax, yawn, and repeat.

To induce relaxation and drowsiness. To improve ability to control action of abdominal muscles.

41. HEEL REACH

Sitting, leaning back with weight resting on hands, legs extended and together.

a. Reach with heels, bringing toes back toward body.

b. Rest and shake feet lightly.

c. Simultaneously, reach with right heel and point left toe; reverse; continue in rhythm.

To stretch heel cord and muscles of back of leg. To activate small muscles of feet.

42. FLAT-FOOT SQUAT

Keeping back erect and heels on ground, bend hips, knees and ankles and attempt to sit down. Lower body as far as possible, "bounce" up slightly, push down a little farther, bounce, down, bounce, down as far as possible. Do not incline trunk forward. (It is easy to sit down if trunk is brought forward, but that is not the purpose of this exercise.)

To stretch heel cord and gastrocnemius muscle.

43. SEAL

Sitting erect, knees bent and soles of feet against each other close to buttocks.

a. Keeping soles of feet together, extend legs until knees are straight.

b. Holding this position of legs, move them apart and bring them back together again, slapping soles of feet together.

To strengthen muscles that support main arch of foot.

44. PLAY THE PIANO

Sitting, knees bent, feet flat on floor.

a. Begin by spreading toes as far apart as possible.

b. Place little toe on floor with foot turned up and other toes spread.

c. Successively bring toes to floor from little toe to big toe, as if playing scale on piano.

d. Slap whole foot lightly on floor, and shake it to relieve any cramps.

e. Repeat with other foot.

f. Repeat, playing with both feet simultaneously.

To activate and improve tonus of small muscles of feet.

45. PARTNER STRETCH

Sit, facing partner, legs extended and soles of feet placed against soles of partner's feet.

a. Keeping legs straight, reach forward and shake hands with right hand.

b. Reach forward and shake left hands.

c. Reach forward and shake both hands.

d. Holding both hands, pull partner toward you; reverse pull and let partner pull you, keeping buttocks on floor.

e. Continue rocking back and forth.

To stretch heel cords and muscles of back of leg. To improve tone of abdominal muscles.

46. BILLIG STRETCH

Standing with left side toward wall or other firm support, feet together and about eighteen inches from wall, knees locked in hyperextension, hips "tucked" under.

Place left arm against wall, shoulder height, with palm of hand, forearm, and elbow in firm contact with wall. Place right hand against hollow of right hip joint. Slowly and deliberately push hips forward and toward wall, as far as they will go—and then just a little bit farther. Slowly return to starting position. At all times keep knees locked and shoulders at right angle to wall.

Three times to right. Three times to left. Three times daily.

To prevent dysmenorrhea. To increase mobility of pelvic girdle and hip joint.

Suggestions for Further Reading

BILLIG, HARVEY E., JR., and EVELYN LOEWENDAHL: *Mobilization of the Human Body*. Stanford University, Calif.: Stanford University Press, 1949.

DUGGAN, ANNE S., MARY ELLA MONTAGUE, and ABBIE RUTLEDGE: *Conditioning Exercises for Girls and Women*. New York: A. S. Barnes and Company, 1945.

FASH, BERNICE: *Body Mechanics in Nursing Arts*. New York, McGraw-Hill Book Company, Inc., 1946.

FISHBEIN, MORRIS (ed.): *Your Weight and How to Control It*. New York: Doubleday & Company, Inc., 1949.

JACOBSON, EDMUND: *You Must Relax*. New York: McGraw-Hill Book Company, Inc., 1948.

LANE, JANET: *Sitting Pretty*. New York: John Wiley & Sons, Inc., 1939.

LANE, JANET: *Your Carriage, Madam!* New York: John Wiley & Sons, Inc., 1947.

MOREHOUSE, LAURENCE, and JOHN M. COOPER: *Kinesiology*. St. Louis: The C. V. Mosby Company, Medical Publishers, 1950.

MORTON, DUDLEY: *Oh Doctor! My Feet!* New York: Appleton-Century-Crofts, Inc., 1939.

NYE, DOROTHY: *Your Aches*. New York: Funk & Wagnalls Company, 1949.

Phi Delta Pi *Symposium on Dysmenorrhea*. Chicago: Phi Delta Pi (5936 N. Kilpatrick Ave.), 1950.

RATHBONE, JOSEPHINE L.: *Relaxation*. New York: Teachers College, Columbia University, 1943.

Index